A Helpful Guide to a
Happy Baby

Practical wisdom from
a maternity nurse for
0-3 months

First published in 2014 by Cooke Publishing as *What Would Fiona Do?*
This new, revised edition published in 2018 by Orphans Publishing

10 9 8 7 6 5 4 3 2

A Cataloguing in Publication record for this book
is available from the British Library.

ISBN: 978 1 903360 29 3

Designed, printed and bound by Orphans Press

Orphans Press
Enterprise Park
Leominster
Herefordshire
HR6 0LD

www.orphanspublishing.co.uk

A Helpful Guide to a
Happy Baby

Practical wisdom from
a maternity nurse for
0-3 months

Fiona Cooke

Orphans
Publishing

About the Author

Fiona Cooke trained as a midwife but soon realised that caring for babies post-birth, and helping their families, was her calling. A mother of two, she is now a maternity nurse with years of experience with families of all shapes, sizes, cultures and backgrounds, and a rosta of glowing client recommendations. Fiona is absolutely passionate about supporting new parents to find their own way to care for their individual babies.

www.fionacooke.co.uk

*To all of the parents who have allowed me into
their lives at such a precious time, and to all of
their beautiful babies.*

*And to my daughters, Hollie and Charlotte,
because my passion for babies started with them.
The trials and joys of parenting them made me
the person and the maternity
nurse that I am today.*

Contents

"I think of Fiona as a 'baby whisperer';
she understands instinctively what a baby
needs or wants, and babies are always
so happy with her."

Delphine, mother of William, Alexander and Constance

Introduction

The best job in the world . . .

Congratulations!

This is such a special time in your life, and I hope to share with you some practical wisdom from my years of experience as a maternity nurse, and give you the confidence to find your own way as parents to your new baby as you get to know them in the first few days, weeks and months.

I have the best job in the world: I help parents with their newborn babies in their own homes. Once women are home from the hospital, or have had their baby at home, I arrive and live in with the family. I am on duty day and night and stay for just a few days or for up to six weeks and sometimes longer – whatever the family needs I will do my best to provide.

I know that the initial postnatal period can feel quite scary if you are alone and trying to recover from the birth and feed your baby with no professional support. You have been preparing and looking forward to this moment for months. It's an amazing miracle and you are holding the most precious thing in your arms. But although this is really exciting it can also be very daunting. The realisation that this little being will rely on you for its every need means the responsibility can be overwhelming.

There will be times when you are not sure why your baby is crying – why are they awake when everyone else is trying to sleep? Your baby surely can't be hungry as they have only just fed! There will be times when you feel absolutely exhausted but your baby wants to feed all evening, or will not settle.

Don't worry, it is all normal. Every new parent goes through the same thing.

I have been asked many times by the families I work with: 'Why haven't you written a book?' Sometimes, after I have left them, parents tell me they think 'What would Fiona do?' when they come across a problem, or when something with their baby is changing. So I have written this book for parents who are expecting or have just had a new baby.

I am putting my knowledge and experience on paper in the hope that I can help as many new parents out there as possible enjoy their babies and take some of their worries away.

As a new parent you will be very busy and all your time will be consumed by caring for your baby, so I have kept this book as clear and concise as I can so you can flick through to the appropriate pages quickly. This book focuses on the first days to three months only, the crucial time when I am working closely with families as a maternity nurse. This period of adjustment to having a new baby in your family is when the most advice and support is needed. I cover everything that you will need to know in the first days, weeks and months. Lots of books are big and thick and have information that covers everything for the first year and beyond. This book has lots of information, but it focuses on just the first three months, just when you need it.

I believe you don't have to stress about a strict routine, but at the same time putting some structure into your days will enable you and baby to know what is happening.

This will give you the confidence to care for your baby, and when you are confident, your baby feels safe and secure. Use this book to help you find what works for you and your baby, as we are all different. My advice will help you guide your baby gently into a flexible routine so that you can get on with everyday things, go shopping or meet someone for a coffee, keep appointments or go to classes, or just fit in with the rest of the family and older siblings.

Remember, there is no right way or wrong way to do things as long as it is a safe way. You will find what suits you and your family; your baby does not know any different, so relax and enjoy these first weeks.

About Me: From Midwife to Maternity Nurse

I knew I wanted to help mothers with their babies after the birth of my own children. I studied midwifery with that intention, but realised that it did not allow me to help parents the way that I intended. Midwives are wonderful, and a great support during pregnancy and birth, but their involvement with mothers and babies has to stop soon after the baby is born. When I found maternity nursing in 2006 I knew it was for me; this is what I was meant to do. I have since worked with hundreds of parents and their babies, and it is such an honour and privilege to have helped them care for their newborns at this special time in their family life.

As a maternity nurse I help parents with their newborn in the home. I am there to help take care of both mum and baby, making sure she has lots of rest and is eating well to enable her to care for her baby. I can support the rest of the family too and offer reassurance. I am there to advise but ultimately to allow parents find what works for them and their individual baby, and to allow them to enjoy those first weeks after the birth, taking away the anxieties that can come with having a new baby in the home.

I will teach parents all they need to know about having a new baby: how to change a nappy, how to bathe baby safely, how to settle the baby with other siblings, and simple things like going out to appointments or getting out of the house on time with a newborn. I am there to help, encourage and support, giving parents the confidence to take care of their baby themselves. I give support and advice to parents on feeding their babies, whether breast or bottle, and can help with common problems. I have extensive experience with breastfeeding mothers, and in the early days I am with mothers day and night, often for several weeks. I have found that with the right support any problem can be overcome, and I will support a mother with all her choices on how to care for her individual baby.

I have experience working with all kinds of babies from all kinds of families and all kinds of religions, cultures and backgrounds. Every family and every baby is different: twins or single babies; first babies and new additions to an existing family; premature and low birth-weight babies; babies with reflux and allergies, jaundice, colic, tongue-tie and feeding problems. I will help to find what works for the whole family. I work quite instinctively so will always find a way. I have travelled with families internationally, giving confidence to parents going away for the first time with a new baby. As a maternity nurse I am here to help.

Why I Wrote This Book

Babies are born into all walks of life: different cultures, different religions, different social backgrounds. They are born with their own little personalities. They all share the instinct to cry for food for survival and normal bodily functions, but the rest is learned behaviour. The adults caring for them teach them everything they know. Babies can only learn from their surroundings and the people who care for them. As parents, each of us have expectations of our baby and so the baby will learn to behave according to these expectations. Whether we choose to keep our baby close to us all the time and co-sleep (attachment parenting) or would like our baby to follow a strict routine when baby eats and sleeps at certain times in a cot or pram, or whether we choose to parent somewhere in between, we expect our baby to slot into our family life what ever kind of background or culture we have.

When I first published a book, it was because my clients were saying I should. I had worked with quite a lot of new parents who wanted their babies on strict routines and were following books that promised to help them achieve this. I saw many new mums getting quite stressed when the baby was awake and crying when he should be sleeping according to the routine, and fast asleep when he should have been awake and feeding. But a tiny new baby cannot go on a strict sleep schedule straight away, especially when breastfeeding as the breastfeeding needs to be established first. A happy contented baby has a full tummy and if they are left hungry then you will not have a happy baby, no matter what the routine 'should' be. So it's vital to work with your own individual baby.

My mantra is that whatever works for the parents and the baby is the right way. We are given lots of advice all the time, but you must only use what works for you. If you do something and your baby is not happy then try another way.

A practical gentle way that works is to introduce a feeding routine that can be flexible to changes, rather than a sleeping schedule.

A flexible feeding routine definitely helps everyone to know roughly what is happening, and can work whatever your own cultural background or parenting expectations. If your baby is fed well then they will sleep well and be a very happy baby. A happy baby equals a happy mummy and a happy mummy equals a happy family.

I'll guide you through the steps to creating a gentle routine that works for you alongside other practical tips and useful information.

Remember:

Every child is different.

This book is intended for advice only.

Listen to your baby and trust your instinct as a parent.

"Fiona has considerable experience and was able to offer me very sound and helpful advice … she leaves us with a very happy and contented baby in a very good routine."

Selina, mother of Lily

Getting Ready

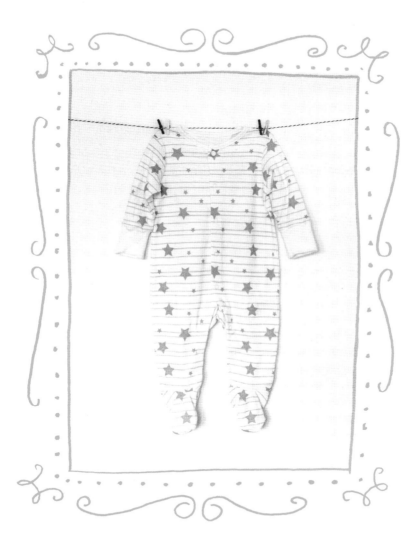

*Being prepared will make
you feel confident.*

Checklist

A short list of the minimum you should have on hand for your newborn baby. There are more things you can buy that might be useful, but there's no need to stock up on everything until you know you will need it. These are my 'essentials' kit list.

Feeding

- Bottles (anti-colic and BPA-free)
- Breast pump (portable, which mimics the natural suck of the baby)
- Breast milk storage bags (if you intend to express regularly and store for longer than a day)
- Steriliser (steam, microwave, or cold water-based)
- Citric acid or white wine vinegar to descale steam steriliser (not needed for microwave or cold-water sterilisers)

For You

- Breast pads
- Nipple cream
- Fitted nursing bras
- Maternity pads

Baby Clothes

- Vests (6)
- Sleep suits (6)
- Cardigans (2)
- Muslin cloths (10)
- Hat

Bathing and Changing

- Newborn nappies (2 packs of 54)
- Cotton wool or water-based wipes
- Nappy bin
- Towels (2)
- Barrier cream
- Changing mat
- Baby bath or baby seat for large bath
- Top and tail bowl
- Changing bag

Sleeping

- Crib or moses basket (used until approximately 4 months, depending on size of baby)
- Mattress protector
- Fitted bottom sheets (2)
- Swaddling sheets (2)
- Cotton cellular blankets (2)

Activity

- Car seat
- Pram, travel system or pushchair
- Baby chair or bouncer
- Sling or carrier (supportive for baby and for your back)
- Mobile or baby gym (ones with music or nature sounds will stimulate your baby at awake times)

Baby Essentials

As you prepare for your baby's birth, and look forward to meeting your new family member, there are lots of things to get ready. Try not to be overwhelmed, but use the following pages as a guide to the practical items you might want to have on hand for the first few days and weeks, and some background reading to understand more about newborn babies and their needs.

Bottles and sterilisers

Even if you intend to breastfeed, a steriliser and a couple of bottles are useful to have on hand. There are a great many bottles on the market – choose ones which are anti-colic and BPA-free, and get the smallest first flow teats for a newborn. There will be time to experiment later if baby decides they might like a different shape or teat, so no need to stock up. When choosing a steriliser, find one which works for you and your routine and lifestyle – you can get steam sterilisers or microwave ones, or a container with cold water and sterilising tablets.

Steam sterilisers are good for frequent users. You need to leave them out on the kitchen worktop near an electric supply and they take from 8 to 12 minutes. Follow the instructions for your appliance. You will also need to descale them once a month depending on how much you use them. Microwave sterilisers are small, portable and you can use them, wash them and put them away after use. They also sterilise very quickly, in 5 minutes or less (again, see your appliance instructions). These are great if you do need to sterilise quite often, but have limited space. A cold-water container and sterilising tablets is recommended for just occasional use, but great to have on hand if you intend to breastfeed primarily.

Car seats

These are the safest way for your baby to travel in a car, and a legal requirement in the UK and other countries. There are lots of seats on the market, and you will need a Group 0+ for a newborn. In most places, hospital rules means you cannot leave without a car seat for your newborn, so it is best to be prepared with the seat ready and fitted in your car. Maxi-Cosi is a brand that fits most pushchair and travel systems, making it convenient to transfer your baby from car to pram without disturbing them. However, newborns should not be left in car seats for long periods, even if they are sleeping peacefully, so aim to keep time in the car seat under an hour.

Changing bag for out and about
You will need:-

- A folding changing mat, towel or disposable mat
- At least two nappies (more if you are out for a long day)
- Water-based nappy wipes
- Barrier cream
- Nappy bags
- A change of clothes, vest and sleep suit
- Muslin cloths
- Bottles of formula, if bottle-feeding (cartons of readymade formula, or pre-measured water with measured powdered formula in a dispenser)
- Soother or dummy, if using
- A toy

Clothing

You will need to dress your baby appropriately for the temperature. If you are wearing extra layers in the winter because you are cold, then your baby will need extra layers. Vest, sleep suit and cardigan if necessary. When going out, put a hat on them and a winter suit if in a carrier, or hat and cardigan if in a pram, with two layers of blankets. Check your baby's temperature to make sure they are not too hot when wrapped so well, by placing your hand on their chest. Always remove a hat when indoors as your baby will become too hot. The same applies in summer when it is hot and you wear as little as possible, so your baby may only need a nappy and vest, or just a nappy. Buy clothes appropriate to the season, and remember that comfortable clothing is best for small babies.

Dummies or soothers

Some people love them, some people hate them. I don't like a baby to rely on a dummy to get to sleep, but when a baby is small they like to suck. Some babies feed and when they are full, they are settled and will go off to sleep without the need of a dummy. However, some will like to suck even when they are not hungry. If you are breastfeeding, and you have the time and don't mind your baby on your breast constantly, then great, but a lot of mothers find this tiring so I would say it's okay to give your baby a dummy. Do what makes life easier – it may only be temporary. However, I would not recommend using a dummy when first establishing breastfeeding. Generally if your baby is crying in the first few weeks he will be hungry.

Once baby is feeding, in a reasonable routine and is more alert and playing, it's time to reduce it. At around 7 to 8 weeks your baby should have good control of their hands so they can suck their fingers or thumb when they wake and soothe themselves back to sleep. Also, they are not so desperate for food like they were as newborns, so can learn to settle themselves. By 9 weeks, I recommend making sure you have got rid of the dummy. However, if it starts to become a problem before that, and your baby starts waking when it drops out, then get rid of it. When your baby is dropping off, pull the dummy out gradually, or you can get rid of it altogether in one go and say the baby doesn't have the dummy even to drop off.

Nappies

Babies use around 6 to 12 nappies a day in the first few months. Many nappy brands make special nappies for newborns. These have a small cut-out at the front of the nappy, to stop it irritating your baby's umbilical cord stump. These nappies tend to be quite small. So if your newborn is on the larger side, they may not fit them for long. You'll find that simply folding down the front of a regular nappy works just as well. An average newborn would usually wear a size 1 nappy, but you can get nappies which are smaller, and if your baby comes early you can also get tiny nappies for premature babies. A weight guide is usually given on the packet.

Your baby will wear nappies for at least two years, so nappies will be a big part of your life for a while, and you will want to make a decision about cloth or disposable.

Cloth nappies (or reusable or washable nappies) can be used again and again, making them a popular choice for eco-conscious parents. But the disadvantage of this is that you have to wash them! Cloth nappies come in a huge range of colours and fabrics, and can be just as easy to put on and take off as disposables, although you may need to change them more frequently. You'll need around 16 to 24 cloth nappies in total. There are four types of reusable nappies: all-in-one nappies, where the inner and outer layers are sewn together, making them one piece; pocket nappies, into which a liner is inserted; shaped nappies, which are most similar to disposable nappies and shaped to a baby's body, with an elasticated waist and legs, and can be fastened with Velcro or poppers; and traditional flat or pre-fold nappies, which are the cheapest type of reusable nappies. To find out more about the wide variety of reusable nappies available, I recommend The Nappy Lady website (www.thenappylady.co.uk)

Disposable nappies, as the name suggests, can simply be thrown away, making them a convenient choice and allowing you to wrap up waste hygienically. These are usually plastic-based.

A lot of parents like to start with disposable nappies at least while their baby is newborn, and then move on to cloth nappies as they get older. There are pros and cons to each type of nappy, and even the environmental benefits or costs will depend on whether you choose a bio degradable eco-friendly disposable or a big brand plastic-based nappy, whether you use a nappy-laundering service or wash them yourself, or if you use reusables for one child or more.

Pram, pushchair or travel system

A pram or pushchair for a newborn must lie flat. This means you will need either a travel system that has a carrycot you can lift on and off a base, or a pushchair that lies flat and is designed for a baby from birth. The choice is very personal to you, depending on your needs. Choose one that is practical for your circumstances, don't just go for one that looks good. Take the time to visit a large store where you can try them all out; make sure to fold them and push them so you can see what would work for you.

- What is your budget for a pram or pushchair?

- Do you need to fold your pram or pushchair to travel or will you push it straight out of the house to the park or shops?

- Will your pushchair fit through your front door, or take up much room in your house? Will it fit in the boot of the car?

- How easy is it to fold? How heavy is it to carry?

- Are you using the pram mostly on pavements or will you need to push on grass, or uneven surfaces? Do you have lots of steps?

- Are you expecting twins? All these questions apply but twin prams come with the babies side by side or one in front of the other, so your preference counts here too.

My personal all-time favourite is the City Jogger Mini. It has three sturdy wheels. It is lightweight and easy to push and steer. The seat of the pushchair lies completely flat and is suitable for a newborn but you can also attach a carrycot if you prefer. It is slim and easy to get in and out of shops, and to store in the car or house, but sturdy enough for a power walk in the park. The best thing however is that it folds very easily: you can lift the carrycot off with one hand or lift your baby into your arms and collapse the whole pushchair with one hand. Very practical.

Sling or carrier

Babies love to be cuddled closely. You can get an array of structured carriers, stretchy slings and wraps which will allow you to have your hands free whilst also keeping your baby close if they need it. Newborn babies should face your body and have their hips and legs supported well. Some people prefer a more unstructured sling tied with knots, and others like the security of buckles and straps. Just make sure your sling is comfortable for your back as well as your baby.

Focus on Feeding: Breast or Bottle?

How you feed your newborn baby is purely your choice and you should not be made to feel guilty whatever you choose to do. Do what feels right for you. Remember a happy mum, a happy baby.

However, as a maternity nurse and as a mother, I would encourage you to try breastfeeding. How will you know what it's like if you don't try it? If it works for you and you enjoy it, then great, and if not, you can switch to bottle-feeding instead. With the right support I have found that even where there are problems with breastfeeding, they can be overcome, and mums are able to continue to feed their baby. But please don't stress about it if you can't breastfeed or choose not to.

There are many benefits to breastfeeding in the early days. Breastmilk is made up of all the right nutrients for your baby – it is the right temperature, it is free and readily available and it is very easily digested. It also helps move the meconium through your baby's digestive system and has antibodies that are good for your baby's immune system. However, generations have been brought up on 'formula' milk as well, and are just fine, very happy and healthy.

Let's compare the two methods:

Bottle-feeding

Advantages	Disadvantages
Anyone can feed your baby	You have to sterilise and make up bottles
You don't have to worry about breastfeeding in public	You have to pay for it
You can see how much your baby is drinking	You have to throw it away if not used
Baby feeds quickly	If not sterilised or kept at the wrong temperature can cause stomach upsets
It can be quicker to establish a routine	Babies can take in air from the bottle which causes wind

Breastfeeding

Advantages	Disadvantages
It's always available	Can get engorged and painful breasts
It's the right temperature and it is sterile	Sore nipples
It is made especially for your baby and has all the right nutrients	Only the mother can feed the baby
It has antibodies to boost immune system	Can be time-consuming
It's easily digested, less windy for your baby	Can be tiring
It's free	Some people may not like feeding in public places so it might limit where you go
It produces hormones that help you relax	It is hard to tell how much a baby has eaten
Has health benefits to the mother	Clothes need to be breastfeeding accessible
You use calories to feed your baby	
The uterus contracts quicker	

Bottle-feeding is quite straightforward if you choose to do so (see pages 32–33) so in this section I'm going to look in detail at breastfeeding, so you can understand more about this way of feeding your baby.

Anatomy and physiology of the breasts

I believe it is important for you to understand how your breast produces milk so you can feel confident when feeding your baby. Your breast is not like a bottle where it is full then empty; your breast continues to make milk, so even though they may not feel as full at the end of the feed as they did at the beginning, be confident that there is always milk coming. The shape and size of your breast really doesn't matter. When it comes to feeding your baby you can be flat-chested and your breasts will still make enough milk for your baby. Large breasts will also make enough milk for your baby. The size of your breast is no indicator as to how much milk you will produce. Babies will feed enough to make sure the breast gives them the correct amount for their needs – if they want more, they will feed more to stimulate more milk to be produced on a supply and demand basis.

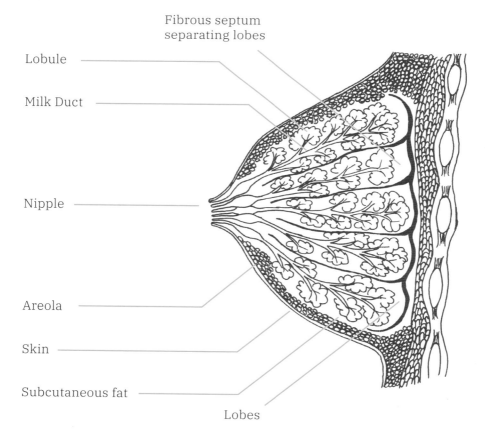

Fibrous septum
separating lobes

Lobule

Milk Duct

Nipple

Areola

Skin

Subcutaneous fat

Lobes

The breast is a secreting gland and is made up of approximately 20 lobes. Each lobe is divided into lobules, which look like cauliflowers and consists of alveoli and ducts. Inside the alveoli are acini cells and it is these that produce the milk. Each acini cell is surrounded by myoepithelial cells; these contract to propel or squeeze the milk into the ducts towards the nipple where it collects in the ampulla just under the areola – the brown part surrounding your nipple. Milk is then expelled through the lactiferous tubules in the nipple and into your baby's mouth. The acini cells are constantly making more milk.

When your baby sucks at the breast, messages are sent along the nerve pathways to the brain. The pituitary gland in the brain produces hormones called prolactin and oxytocin. The hormone prolactin stimulates the acini cells to produce milk. The hormone oxytocin (the same hormone which produces contractions of the uterus in labour) stimulates the myoepithelial cells around the acini cells to contract and squeeze the milk towards the nipple where it flows out of the nipple to your baby.

Letdown reflex and learning to relax

For the milk to 'let down' when the baby starts suckling, you need to be relaxed. Oxytocin is the 'feel good' hormone, the hormone of love. It kicks in when baby starts to suck and the muscles contract around the cells to allow the milk to flow. When you feel relaxed and well, or when your baby goes onto the breast and it feels nice as you are enjoying the closeness, your body will produce more oxytocin and in return this oxytocin makes you feel even more relaxed and well. Oxytocin is vital for the letdown reflex. So when your baby starts to feed your brain tells the pituitary gland in the brain to stimulate oxytocin, then the oxytocin causes little contractions in the breast which squeeze the milk in your breast towards the nipple where milk will drip out easily. Some women describe this letdown feeling as a tingling in the breast and it can sometimes happen just by hearing the sound of your baby crying or before a feed when your breasts are full.

However, I also have seen women with full to bursting breasts and milk that seemingly just won't come out. The baby is shouting at the breast and mum is worried she has no milk. Even when trying to express, her milk just won't come. I liken this scenario to when your bladder is full to bursting. Imagine you have been travelling for hours and you are desperate for a wee, you can't hold it any longer. You stop the car, there are no toilets, you are in the middle of nowhere, and you think – 'I have GOT to go!' You get out of the car and try to find somewhere suitable, but there is nowhere private. You know passing traffic can see you but still you think, 'I really have to go'. So you prepare yourself and, low and behold, it won't come – you cannot wee even though you are desperate. You are too anxious and your body won't let it out because the muscles that hold it in won't relax.

For the breast to letdown its milk, you need to be relaxed and not anxious. So never think you don't have milk there; you almost certainly do, but you need to believe it will flow, relax and let it out.

Hopefully you will find breastfeeding really easy and have no problems and your milk will just flow so you will wonder what I am talking about!

There is more in-depth information in the following chapters on posititioning and latching your baby, and common stumbling blocks. Remember that breastfeeding may have a steep learning curve but it is a wonderful way to feed your baby, so give it a try if you possibly can, at least in the early days, but don't worry if for some reason you can't – you will still be able to feed your baby closely and lovingly if you use a bottle instead. Being close to your baby giving cuddles, chatting, holding, feeding and skin to skin contact all stimulate oxytocin, which makes you feel good. When you feel good you will enjoy your baby, which helps with bonding for both mother and father. Touch and closeness is the food of love: it stimulates the senses. A baby can see your face from 12 inches away as a newborn and continues to see more each day. Your baby will feel loved and content and safe and secure knowing you are close however you feed them if you give them plenty of time, closeness and attention.

Remember:

Being prepared will make you feel confident.

Consider trying to breastfeed first if you can.

Relax!

"As a result of Fiona's presence, we have become very knowledgeable and confident parents. Fiona helped us to truly enjoy this special time with our newborn."

Nina, mother of George and Viola

The First Few Days

Feeding, nappies – lots of nappies! –
swaddling and bathtime.

Calm and Confident

Congratulations! Your baby is here. It's a wonderful feeling to hold them after so long, and now you can start to get to know them and their unique personality.

Try to be calm and relaxed with your baby; if you are confident then your baby will feel safe. Your baby just wants to eat and sleep and poo so you need to guide your baby into a pattern that suits you and your family. Babies can't do it on their own.

You will be given lots of advice from everyone and anyone. Take what suits you and ignore the rest. You know your baby better than anyone and you are the only one who can find what is right for you and your family.

Understanding Newborns

Contained in a warm environment in your womb, surrounded by soft but firm muscles and floating in amniotic fluid, your baby is feeding constantly via the umbilical cord from the placenta, gaining all the necessary nutrients and oxygen. They are held tightly in the womb, which is very noisy. Your baby is constantly jiggled around when you walk or move. Babies are born at 40 weeks because if they stayed within the mother longer, the mother would not be able to birth them. But when babies are born, they are really not quite mature enough to cope with the world – some experts call the first three months after birth the 'fourth trimester', as newborns mature enough outside the womb to get used to our world.

Cuddle, jiggle and rock your baby whenever they want it – don't worry, you cannot spoil a newborn baby. Enjoy these first few weeks of cuddles and be patient: don't expect too much, too soon. Give them time to adjust to this out-of-the-womb world.

First Feeds

Days 1 and 2 – colostrum

When your baby is born, they will probably want to feed within the first hour of life. At this stage your breasts contain colostrum, a thick yellowish liquid with all the nutrients, fats, sugars, vitamins and minerals, antibodies and proteins that your baby needs for the first three to four days. This first milk coats the lining of the stomach and intestine, protecting it from pathogens; it also helps the gut to continue to mature.

Colostrum is very important, so even if you intend to bottle-feed, it is great to try feeding your baby at the breast when they are first born so that they can benefit from this natural protection.

Your baby only needs a tiny amount to keep energy levels up and their little stomachs can only hold small amounts, so little and often is the key. All babies are different: some will have a 5-minute feed on each breast and sleep for hours and others will feed on and off every hour for hours on end. This is normal, let them feed as often as they like. Get yourself comfortable before you start. Grab a glass of water, a snack, the remote, your phone, magazines, whatever you might need as this can sometimes take an hour or more in the early days. When sitting up to feed you will need a comfortable supportive chair, and you may need pillows behind you to support your shoulders. Placing a pillow on your lap and lying your baby across it will bring them closer to you and prevent you from leaning forwards and causing back and shoulder pain. You can get V-shaped feeding pillows (which are also good in pregnancy for sleeping and supporting your bump) but a regular pillow will do the job just as well. Breastfeeding does get easier as your baby gets more efficient at sucking, and your milk will flow more freely as the weeks go by, but at the beginning it can be lengthy so sit back, be patient and enjoy this time; it doesn't last forever.

Positioning baby on the breast

If you are about to feed on your left breast then use your right hand to hold your baby across your body with your baby facing the left breast, with the left hand use your thumb and finger to shape your breast so it is easier for your baby to latch on. (Do the opposite if you are feeding from your right breast). Holding your baby at the shoulders, bring them towards the breast. As their mouth opens, bring your baby closer to latch onto the breast. Once baby is sucking and is 'on' correctly and comfortable, you can relax both arms and shoulders. If you have very large breasts you may need to continue to hold the breast, as when you loosen it, it will drop and pull away from baby's mouth.

You know your baby is latched correctly as you will hear him sucking and swallowing. It should not hurt but may feel a little odd at first. Relax and take your time.

For more detailed information on problem-solving breastfeeding issues, see page 83–86.

Days 1 and 2 – bottle-feeding

If you have chosen to bottle-feed you will probably be encouraged by your midwife to feed your baby within an hour of birth. You will need to choose a formula to give your baby – it may be a small choice at the hospital, so you might want to take with you some cartons of ready-made formula of a brand that your friends or family have already used with their babies. There are no 'wrong' choices, just preferences. You will also need some sterilised bottles.

For more detailed instuctions on sterilising and making up formula from powder, see page 32–33

To bottle-feed your baby, make yourself comfortable: it could take 5 minutes for your baby to drain the bottle or it may take an hour. Some babies will 'guzzle' really quickly, burp, and they are done; others will slowly feed, slowly burp, then need a 20-minute rest before finishing the rest of the bottle.

Sit comfortably, hold your baby cradled in your arms with their head slightly higher than their body. Offer the teat to your baby; if they are hungry they will root towards the teat. This is a natural rooting reflex, where the baby will open their mouth and try to latch on to the teat like they might to a nipple if you were breastfeeding. Put the teat in your baby's mouth and hold the bottle upside down so the milk drains towards the teat. Making sure that the teat is full of milk all the time is important so that your baby is not sucking in air, as this will cause wind. Let your baby feed and suck for as long as they like – they might finish the bottle in one go or, more likely, stop halfway through. You then need to sit your baby upright so they can burp freely, or put your baby on your shoulder to burp. (For more on bringing up wind, see page 34–35.)

For your baby's very first feed, only allow your baby to drink a small amount (30–40mls) as their stomach is so tiny. This will be sufficient to keep your baby's blood sugar levels up, after the long exhausting journey of birth. If you allow your baby to drink a full feed (90mls) it is likely they will vomit most of it back because the stomach is so small and needs to stretch as baby grows.

After this feed your baby may sleep anything from 2 to 5 hours. I would wake baby and give them a feed if they have slept for 4-5 hours, as a baby's blood sugars can drop quickly if they go a long time without food in the first 24 hours after birth.

For the next feed, you can allow baby to take a little more milk, maybe 40–50mls. Increase each feed depending on what your baby is drinking e.g. if they take 40mls at the first feed, I would expect them to drink the same at the next feed, or perhaps a little more. If your baby then takes 50mls comfortably and keeps it down, I would subsequently offer 60mls at the next feed.

In the first 24 hours your baby may be very sleepy after the first feed but, by day 2, your baby will probably want to feed every 2 to 3 hours, and may even last up to 4 hours before next feed.

Timing Feeds

Using when your baby last fed to establish a routine is useful, and we time the gaps between feeds from the beginning, when your baby last began to feed. So if your baby woke to feed at 11:00, for instance, and fed for 40 minutes or an hour or even longer, sucking and swallowing and drinking milk all of this time before falling back to sleep, then typically they might not demand another feed until three or even four hours from the start of that last feed. Your baby would be hungry sometime between 14:00 and 15:00, a 3 to 4 hour interval from 11:00. In these early days, I would wake a newborn baby at 4 hours if they have not woken naturally, to make sure the baby feeds often and continues to gain weight well.

Days 3 to 4 – producing milk

Each day your breasts will start to produce more milk and you will need to wear a good supportive bra. Your breasts will become very full and may feel quite uncomfortable at approximately 3 days post-birth. This is called engorgement. You can hand-express a tiny amount, and try putting hot or cold flannels on your breasts. This can be comforting. There is also the old-fashioned remedy of cabbage leaves from the fridge inside your bra – crush the stalks to release the juice (they don't smell very nice but it does ease the pain).

You may find that you are very tearful and emotional, as days 3 to 4 post-birth are typically what we call 'the baby blues'. This will not last long, maybe a day or two. You may feel you are crying for no reason – this is completely normal.

If you haven't put your baby to the breast, your body will now start to adjust itself and stop producing milk, and your breasts will begin to return to their pre-pregnancy, pre-birth size.

If you are breastfeeding, by day 3 to 4, your breasts will feel quite full of milk and you will be able to hear your baby swallowing the milk when feeding. Your baby will probably feed for approximately 15 to 20 minutes on each breast. Others may feed for less time and some will feed for longer, up to 1 hour or more, at the breast. Let them feed as little or as often as they like for these early days.

Your baby will want to feed for a little longer at the breast and will then sleep for a little longer between feeds, maybe 2 hours or, if you are lucky, 3 to 4 hours. Some babies feed very little and sleep a lot in these early days and others want to eat constantly.

Bottle-feeding with formula

If you are bottle-feeding, let's look more closely at preparing feeds and the routine.

To bottle-feed you will need at least 6 bottles. The number one priority with bottle-feeding is sterilising your baby's bottles so there are no bacteria on them that your baby could ingest, which could then cause an upset stomach, vomiting or diarrhoea. Vomiting and diarrhoea is far more serious for a baby than for an adult, as babies can become dehydrated very quickly and will need to be admitted to hospital because they have become seriously sick, so wash your hands and keep baby's feeding equipment clean and sterile.

It is a good idea to try to prepare a feed at least half an hour before your baby will be hungry and shouting for food, so approximately 2.5 to 3 hours after the beginning of the last feed.

Boil the kettle and leave to stand for 15 to 20 minutes so the water is not boiling but still hot (it will be at around 70°C). There is nothing worse than a screaming baby when you have to wait for the water to cool.

1. First wash your hands.
2. Wash bottles with warm soapy water using a bottle brush, and rinse well.
3. Sterilise, using your chosen equipment e.g. steam steriliser, microwave steriliser or cold water steriliser (see page 12). You will need to sterilise the bottles every 24 hours. I tend to do them first thing in the morning but you might prefer to do them in the evening or another time. Find a time that works well for you and try to do them routinely at roughly the same time each day. If you have used any bottles, or think they have been touched or contaminated in any way e.g. you dropped it and the teat touched the floor, then you will need to re-sterilise.
4. Once the bottles are sterile, using clean hands, put all the bottles together – teats screwed on, lids closed – so they are ready when

you need them. This will avoid contaminating the other bottles every time you open the lid of the steriliser if you are only taking one out at a time.

5. When preparing each feed use freshly boiled water but allow it to cool for 15–20 minutes so it is not scalding. Measure the correct amount of cooled boiled water into the bottle. Be very careful as the water is still hot.

6. Add the required amounts of powder as per the instructions on the packet – in the UK this is usually 1oz/30ml of water to 1oz of powder (1 scoop). The guidelines on the formula container will tell you not only how much to give depending on the age of your baby, but also how much for the weight of your baby, so make adjustments if your baby is lighter than average or heavier than average.

7. Screw the teat on and place the cap on the bottle, then shake well to mix all the formula into the water.

8. Place the bottle into a jug of cold water to cool it. The milk should be cool enough that it is not too hot for your baby to drink, but at about the same temperature as breastmilk would naturally be, so approximately 37°C. You can drip some milk through the teat onto your wrist, a sensitive part of your skin. The milk should feel neither hot nor cold, but similar to your body temperature.

9. Feed your baby, and try to finish the feed within an hour.

If you are timing baby's feeds, then the time they start their feed is the time you use, so if baby is on a 3-hourly routine, they would be hungry approximately 3 hours after they started the feed. Any milk that is left after an hour that your baby has not finished should be thrown away, as milk at room temperature or warmed up has an increased risk of growing bacteria and causing an upset stomach. As well as the risk of the formula spoiling, if they are still drinking after an hour of starting the feed they probably won't be hungry again within another three hours from start. By the end of the day you won't know what your baby has had to eat and they could possibly be a whole feed down by the time you go to bed, so your baby might then wake up hungry in the night. So try to establish a routine where you begin a feed, finish within an hour, wind and settle to sleep, then wake for the next feed two hours later, which will be three hours 'between feeds'.

Bringing up wind

It is important to wind your baby well before and after feeding and before they go to sleep, if your baby is to settle well and sleep well. When burping your baby, think of the wind or gas as an air bubble: bubbles travel upwards so you need your baby's oesophagus (the tube from baby's mouth to the stomach) to be straight, so that the bubbles can travel upwards and out through the mouth.

If the bubbles have gone the other direction, downwards, wind will pass along the intestine and this can sometimes be uncomfortable for baby. It will pass out of your baby's bottom eventually but usually not before you have had to listen to your baby crying.

Breastfed babies tend to take in less wind than bottle-fed babies, but you still need to burp them. Wind is not only caused from air taken in from feeding but also from the gas that is produced in the stomach from digestion so even when burped well there can always be another one. All babies generally need to burp after feeding; this is completely normal even an hour or more after a feed. It's also important to make sure there is no wind before starting a feed, so that your baby is comfortable and feeds well.

Let your baby feed for as long as they like on the breast or with the bottle. Don't stop them; your baby will stop feeding when they are ready and take a natural pause. When baby stops feeding, get them upright; as long as their back is nice and straight and upright a burp should come. You can sit your baby up straight on your knee or you could place them over your shoulder.

When sitting baby on your knee, try pushing them forward a little but don't bend the baby over; if you bend baby over too far at the waist, they are likely to bring back some milk. This is called a posit. A little positing is quite normal. The muscle at the top of the stomach is often weak in a newborn, and if it does not shut properly it allows milk to spill back. (Projectile vomiting, if it is a one-off, is nothing to worry about, but if this happens frequently or almost every feed then you should consult a doctor as excessive amounts of milk may mean the muscle is weaker than normal so it would be best to get it checked out.)

1.

Get baby upright. Their back should be straight. Use a muslin cloth over your shoulder in case of positing.

2.

Pat your baby's back gently or stroke firmly upwards.

3.

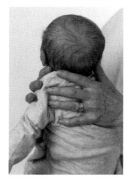

You can also wind by sitting baby up straight on your knee. Support their head.

4.

Try pushing baby a little forward but don't bend them too far at the waist.

There is no need to spend hours trying to get a burp from your baby. In my experience if your baby hasn't burped almost straight away after feeding, they probably don't need to, or the wind just isn't ready to come. When you have finished feeding, tried unsuccessfully to wind them and then settled your baby down to sleep, if your baby does have wind then it will be uncomfortable for them to lie flat so they will wriggle and cry out. Lift your baby up and they should burp easily; then you can put baby back down to sleep.

It's important to remember that burping is normal. Some babies, though, struggle with more wind than others. If your baby is in discomfort but struggles to burp, you will have an uncomfortable baby who cries and you will find it difficult to console him, so you will need to find out why your baby struggles with wind. Is your baby taking in air when feeding? You will hear clicking sounds as air goes into the mouth. Do you need to change position to get a better latch on the breast? Perhaps you need to change the bottles you use as a different shaped teat may help. You can buy anti-colic bottles, which are designed to stop your baby gulping so much air when feeding.

Another cause of excessive wind could be that your baby is producing more gas in the stomach than average. This can be from your diet if you are breastfeeding, or if bottle-feeding you may need to change the formula you use. Speak to your Health Visitor or your GP before changing any element of your diet or your baby's formula.

From the Womb to Our World

During your pregnancy your baby has been very happy in your womb, and why not? Contained in a warm environment, surrounded by soft but firm muscles and floating in amniotic fluid, your baby has been feeding constantly via the umbilical cord from the placenta, gaining all the necessary nutrients and oxygen.

Just before your baby is born it is held tightly in the womb, and when a baby kicks or moves their arms, they push against the walls of the uterus, which protects the baby from danger. It is also very noisy in there and your baby is constantly jiggled around when you walk or move, so it's no surprise that when babies are born, and we expect them to wait for food, sleep in a quiet place in a large basket, and get used to being in a world where there is no motion around them, that this is actually very strange to them and they will cry.

Now is the time to cuddle and jiggle or rock your baby whenever they want it – don't worry, you cannot spoil a newborn baby.

Each week your baby will take bigger feeds and so sleep longer. Baby will learn to sleep anywhere, whether it's noisy or quiet. Enjoy these first few weeks of cuddles and be patient: your baby will do what you want. Just don't expect too much, too soon. Give them time to adjust to this out-of-the-womb world.

Most babies will adjust quite quickly within two to three weeks and fall into a three-hourly feeding pattern. However, some babies will want to feed smaller amounts more frequently, and want more cuddles.

By days three to four, you probably know already that as soon as you pick your baby up into your arms they will stop crying. It's a natural instinct for you. For your baby the feeling of being wrapped in your arms, secure and safe, with a rocking motion to help them easily sleep, is like being in the womb. If your baby is unsettled and will not stop crying you can jiggle them around a little in a continuous rhythm and motion, and if they are crying loudly comfort them by saying 'shhhhhhhh, shhhhhhh', like the whooshing of the umbilical cord from the placenta to the baby. This will normally calm a crying baby. You can also swaddle your baby to mimic the tightness of the womb before placing baby into bed.

Swaddling

I am a great believer in the swaddle and believe it is the reason why many of the babies I care for sleep well and settle into an easy routine. When they are born, babies jerk their little arms and twitch whilst sleeping; this often wakes them up. They can also hit themselves in the face and have no control over these movements. This is called the 'moro' reflex or 'startle' reflex. When babies were in the womb, if they kicked or pushed with their arms or legs, they would feel resistance of the uterus walls and this was a safe secure feeling. Swaddling mimics this, and enables you to put your baby down into a basket, allowing them to feel that same safety and security so you can get on with other things. Baby will also sleep better and longer because they won't be woken up by the 'moro' reflex. When your baby swipes their hands across their face by accident it causes the rooting or sucking reflex and, of course, baby then wants to suck. This can confuse you into thinking your baby is hungry or wants a dummy. Swaddling can eliminate these problems.

Swaddling is a very old traditional method of calming your baby but you must swaddle correctly and safely. The main considerations are sleeping position, temperature and hip position.

Safe sleeping guidelines are that your baby should be placed down to sleep on their back, never on their side or front when swaddled. You must also use a large thin muslin square or cotton sheet and dress your baby appropriate to environmental temperatures so as not to overheat them. Do not swaddle in a traditional blanket.

Swaddling too tightly around the hips with your baby's legs extended out straight can cause their hips to be displaced. When swaddling, your baby should still be able to lift their legs into a frog position. This helps the ball joint at the top of the leg to sit correctly and deeply into the hip socket. Follow the instructions opposite to get the correct method.

Full swaddle with arms tucked down

The full swaddle with arms tucked down is particularly good for a fussy baby; your baby may cry whilst you do it and may cry for a few minutes when you put them down, but they will soon go to sleep and sleep well. If you swaddle firmly around the tops of the arms only and leave the cloth loose around your baby's hips, your baby should be able to pull their legs up and have free movement to kick.

Fold one corner of the swaddle blanket down so you have a straight edge, and the blanket has a triangle shape, the long straight edge at the top.

Lie your baby on it with the shoulders just below the straight edge, arms by their side. The points of the triangles are at your baby's feet and opposite their shoulders.

Fold down one point of the triangle across your baby's body, and over their shoulder, pinning their arm to their side.

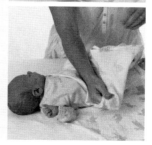

Tuck the point of the triangle under your baby's bottom, pulling it taut.

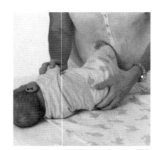

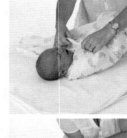

Take the other point of the triangle, and wrap it tightly around the baby's shoulders, pinning their other arm to their side. Leave the hips looser than the shoulders, and the feet loose.

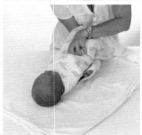

If your baby kicks a lot, you can bring the blanket at their feet up and tuck it into the folds of the swaddle across their chest.

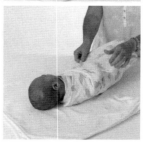

Full swaddle with arms across chest

This is good for a more relaxed baby who needs the comfort but likes their arm up. Follow the steps for a full swaddle but begin with the arms folded across the chest instead of by their side.

Half swaddle

A half swaddle is good for a really chilled out baby who likes to relax their arms above their head and isn't woken by the moro reflex (or for an older baby who now gets their arms out or gets hot).

- Lie baby on folded swaddle blanket, chest/underarms to top edge

- Fold down and tuck under bottom

- Wrap the remaining blanket around the bottom, leaving the arms free

If your baby is a really wriggly sleeper, and moves about a lot, then you can also try tucking the extra swaddle blanket from by their feet under their cot mattress. This stops them moving about.

Some time between about one month to 6 weeks, your baby will have become used to not being in a dark tight place, being jiggled constantly, and will have grown out of this and will settle well in a crib without swaddling.

Safe Sleeping

Research by the Foundation for the Study of Infant Death, now called The Lullaby Trust, suggests the safest way for your baby to sleep is on their back, in the room where you are sleeping.

Cot death is less common in babies who sleep on their backs. Your baby will not choke when laid on their back. If the baby spills a little milk after a feed, they will let it dribble out of the side of their mouth, so it is a good idea to put a muslin cloth on top of the sheet under the baby's head to save changing the whole sheet every time some milk is dribbled. It is recommended that your baby sleeps in your room for the first 6 months. Cigarette smoke is a main risk factor in sudden infant death syndrome, so try to create a smoke-free zone. If you have smokers in the family, get them to smoke outside, and certainly not in the same room as the baby. Ask them to change their clothing and wash their hands before cuddling your baby too. Studies also show that the use of a dummy reduces the risk of cot death but if your baby doesn't want it, don't force it on them (see page 14 for more on dummies).

Sleeping position

Lay your baby's feet so they are just touching the foot of the crib or basket. This way your baby cannot slip down and under the sheets and blankets. Do not use a pillow, just a firm mattress that fits well into the crib, covered with a sheet. To cover your baby, use sheets and thin blankets, NOT a duvet or sleeping bag. Using several layers allows you to add or remove them, depending on the temperature of the room where your baby is sleeping. Tuck the blankets firmly under the sides of the mattress so they don't come loose and move over baby's head. Tuck them up to the baby's shoulders.

Temperature

Babies need to be warm but not too warm. Being too warm increases the risk of cot death. Have the room at the normal temperature you would have it to be comfortable for you. Your baby is wrapped well in the cot so check they are not too hot by putting the back of your hand down their clothing and touching your baby's chest. If baby feels too warm or sticky, remove some bedding or reduce the room temperature. It is OK for baby's hands to feel cold as long as their body is warm.

If your baby has any signs of illness, see a GP:

- Vomiting, especially bile or green vomit
- Taking less fluids and passing less urine
- High-pitched or unusual cry
- Drowsiness, floppiness, or less responsive than usual
- Wheezy, grunting, fast or difficult breathing
- High fever or sweating a lot
- Looking pale or blue

- Blood in the nappies
- Rash

If you feel that your baby is unwell in some way, trust your instinct and get baby checked by a GP, even if their symptoms are not on this list.

Cot death is uncommon but following the safe sleep guidelines will help reduce the risk further. It is rare, so please enjoy your baby.

Nappies

You will need to change your baby's nappy every time they have a poo. If your baby is asleep and you know they have done a poo, leave it until they wake up. Most babies will poo during a feed, but also get sleepy in the middle of the feed so then you can burp and change the nappy, waking baby up to continue feeding.

In the early days, 6 to 8 nappies a day is perfectly normal – you may use more or less. In the night, I would only change baby's nappy if they have done a poo, so try not to disturb your baby too much. You may think it is a long time to have a nappy on without a change, but when your baby is sleeping for 12 hours, you will not want to wake your sleeping baby, so don't worry; it's fine to leave it on if it is only urine. I have assumed you are using disposable nappies, but if you are using cloth nappies, then use lots of barrier cream and change the nappy more frequently to prevent nappy rash.

What should the contents look like?

The first few dirty nappies will be meconium; this is very dark green, almost black, and very sticky and tar-like. Once your baby is eating well this will change to a lighter green, then to yellow. If you are breastfeeding the poo will be very loose and a mustard-seed consistency and may smell quite sweet. If you are using formula, it will be yellow but of slightly pasty consistency and a little more smelly. Your baby should be passing urine constantly.

How to change a nappy

Lie your baby on their back on a changing area – you can use a large towel or changing mat – this can be on a changing table or on the bed or floor, wherever you can find that is suitable. If you are using a changing table, please don't walk away from your baby while they are on it, even if your baby is newborn. It only takes a second for your baby to lift their legs into the air, lean to the side and roll off onto the floor. If you need to leave your baby, place them somewhere safe, in the cot for example.

Undo the tabs of the nappy and peer inside. If baby has done a poo, then use the nappy to try to wipe most of the poo away. Use the front of the nappy to wipe downwards and leave the nappy there tucked closed under the bottom so you have a clean area. I only recommend the use of cotton wool to clean babies under a month and then will introduce water-based baby wipes.

For little girls, wipe from front to back, so wipe downwards towards the bottom, taking soiling away from the vagina. Don't be alarmed if you see a little bloodstained mucous coming from the vagina; this is normal and called a pseudo period. However, if you are concerned speak to a midwife or health professional.

For boys, wipe over and around the penis, lift testicles and clean in the creases. Under the testicles it can get sore here if not cleaned well. (If your little boy has been circumcised, then follow your surgeon's instructions. You can put a little Vaseline in the nappy right in front of the penis so the nappy does not stick to the penis. Keep the nappy area clean as normal. You will be told about any swelling and what to expect, but always if you are concerned speak to your health professional.)

Put a barrier cream on the bottom area if it is looking sore, to heal and protect it. Make sure the skin is dry before applying.

1.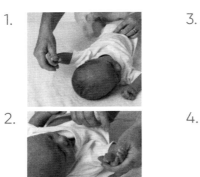

2.

3.

4.

Tips for dressing and undressing

To get a babygro on and off, get baby to grip your thumb. Then you can pull baby's arms through the sleeves.

Wide-necked or 'envelope' vests and babygros mean you can pull the vest off down the baby's body, rather than over their head. If there's been a really messy poo, this stops it being smeared anywhere near their head or upper body.

Let baby be comfortable. Choose stretchy, soft fabrics when they're little. Save the pretty dresses or smart shirts and trousers for when they're older and not spending all their time lying down.

Cord care

You do not need to do anything to the umbilical cord, just keep an eye on it. If it becomes red and sore or is excessively smelly, wet and oozing, tell your midwife or GP. Otherwise, leave it alone. It rots off naturally, so it might smell a little, or just dry out and then drop off. This typically happens between 5 to 14 days but it may take longer if the cord is thick.

Bathing

Babies are born covered in vernix, a white waxy substance made up of skin cells and proteins. This acts like a natural antibacterial ointment and a barrier against bacteria and infections. Vernix is also a natural skin moisturiser, and during the transition from amniotic fluid into the air this stops their skin drying out. Many parents prefer to let the vernix be absorbed by their baby's skin before they do their first bath; in fact, I have not bathed some babies for up to a month on the request of their parents, and just washed them with cotton wool and water around the face, under the chin and under the arms, and of course the nappy area, which is constantly cleaned at each nappy change.

There is no rush to bathe your baby and it should be an enjoyable experience. In fact, bathing a baby too soon after birth can cause low blood sugar, which can make a baby too sleepy to feed, and new babies need to be held skin-to-skin. This is much more important than bathing them. If you gave birth in hospital, delaying baby's first bath means you will be much more relaxed in your home environment, using your own things.

You can wash your newborn baby anywhere, in a sink if large enough, in a large bowl, baby bucket, baby bath or in your adult bath if you can comfortably and safely lean in. Find what works for you.

There is no need to bathe your baby every day. You clean baby's bottom at every nappy change, and you can wipe your baby's face, and under the chin where milk may collect to prevent it getting smelly and sore. Use cotton wool and warm water. I use only water for the first month and avoid harsh soapy products, which can dry out sensitive skin. Bathing every other day is sufficient and even if it is three days or more, that's OK as long as you are wiping them with water in between. As your baby gets to five or six weeks old, it is a good idea to incorporate this into the bedtime routine. A baby loves a bath as much as we do and it can be relaxing for them before bedtime. You might want to bathe one day before bedtime, and massage the next day.

Baby's first bath

The first bath can be a little scary as you might be worried that your baby is slippery and wriggly, but there is nothing to worry about. Just follow the steps below.

Choose a time in the day that suits you and your baby, usually just before a feed (or you may want to give a tiny bit of the feed so you know baby will be happy, then give the rest when you have finished.)

Prepare everything you will need for the bath and have the bathroom at a warm comfortable temperature. Place a large folded towel or changing mat on the floor then place a towel, which you will use to dry baby, on top of this. Lay baby on the towel whilst running the water. Most babies love the sound of running water and often if they are a little unsettled they will lie on a towel happily whilst listening to it. Have a clean nappy and change of clothes in the bathroom too, so you don't have to leave the room.

If your bathroom is not big enough for floor use then you will find your own way to bathe baby. You can prepare baby in another room on the changing mat then carry through to the bathroom wrapped in the towel, then back to the bedroom to dry and dress. Find what works for you.

Run cold water into the bath first to prevent scalding then add hot water. Prepare the bath water to a temperature of 36.5°C to 37.5°C, which is our body temperature. Test this by dipping in your elbow, not your hand. When dipping your elbow into the water, at body temperature it will feel warm on your skin, not too hot and not too cold. Using your hand to gauge the temperature will not be as sensitive as your elbow. You can use a bath thermometer that floats in the water if you prefer.

If the water is too hot or too cold your baby will cry, but a warm bath is nice and relaxing.

I don't recommend adding anything to the water for the first month, so as not to cause any dryness to sensitive skin. Water is sufficient for washing.

Have the water deep enough to submerge your baby's body. Imagine sitting in the bath with hardly any water – it wouldn't be very pleasant. Babies love to be immersed in water, and once they feel secure and safe they will let their body relax and float.

Place baby on the floor or surface where they are safe and cannot roll into danger. When babies are tiny they don't like being naked, so keep baby dressed and warm until you are ready. (Once they are a little older, at 6 weeks plus, then they love to be naked. They feel free without the nappy on and can kick happily. Naked time is fun for a baby.)

So, baby is on the floor listening to running water and watching you happily, then undress baby. First, wash your baby's face with warm water and cotton wool, around the eyes and ears and chin one side, and then use a clean piece of cotton wool for the other side so as not to pass on infection from sticky eyes from one to the other. Clean the nappy area if it's soiled.

Lift baby with one hand supporting the head and neck and your other hand under the bottom, and place baby slowly in the bath then remove your hand from under their bottom. You can continue to hold your hand under baby's head if you feel safe doing so, or you can move that hand across so the baby's head is resting on your forearm or wrist and your fingers are wrapped around baby's upper arm.

Wash baby from head to toe with the other hand. I am right-handed, so I hold baby's head in my left hand and my right hand is free to wash them, scooping water over the hair. They love this. Try not to splash the face. Wash under chin, armpits, creases of elbows, hands, groin and creases behind the knees etc. (I tend not to use sponges on tiny babies, as it is easy to forget which sponge you have used on the bottom area then next time it gets used for the face, which is not good. If you want to use a sponge, make sure it is washed after each bath or have one colour sponge for the face and one for the bottom area.)

Let baby have a little float; you can gently glide baby back and forth in the water. They find this very calming and soothing. Bathe for as little or as long as you like. If you are in a rush then a quick dip in and out is fine but if you have time, and baby is happy, then both of you can enjoy the experience. Don't worry about the umbilical cord. It is fine for it to have a good soak; you don't need to do anything to it, just pat dry around it when baby is out of the bath.

If you choose to use a bath chair or hammock, don't fill the bath too deep as baby will float and lift off the chair. Also your baby's body will not be fully in the water so you can cover their tummy with a flannel so they don't get cold or feel exposed.

Never leave your baby unattended in the bath, not even for a second. They could drown. If the phone rings, ignore it; if someone is at the door, ignore them or lift your baby out of the bath and wrap in the towel, place safely on the floor, or take baby with you in your arms.

Lift your baby out of the bath, one hand under the head and neck, the other under the bottom. Place them on the towel you have laid on the floor and wrap them up (like a bug in a rug), covering their hair as baby will get cold quickly. Dry baby from head to toe, not forgetting to dry the crease behind knees and elbows, as these can get sore if left wet. Roll your baby onto their side to dry their back. Once the umbilical cord has dropped off, which could be anywhere from one to two weeks, depending on the thickness, I then put babies on their tummies for drying and also when massaging. Tummy time is good to strengthen the neck and back muscles; baby will learn to lift their head (see page 91).

If baby is happy after the bath and will allow you to massage them, then great, go ahead. They might want a little feed of an ounce, or 5 to 10 minutes of breast, then you can carry on with the massage (see pages 62–67 for more on the benefits of massage). Once bathed, massaged, dressed and fed, baby will probably fall sound asleep.

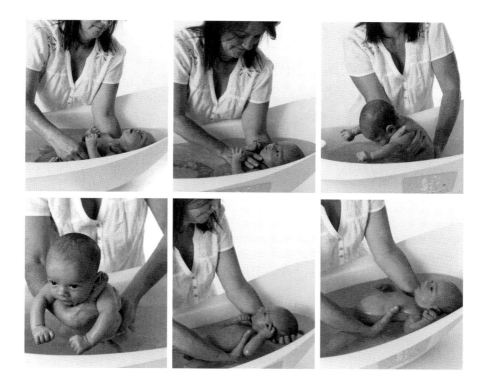

Bathing together

There is no reason why you can't have baby in the bath with you. It's a lovely thing to do and can be a great way for fathers to bond too. Do it safely – get into a nice warm bath of the correct temperature (36.5°C to 37.5°C) and get your partner to pass baby in. Your baby will lie on your tummy or chest happily. Place a warm flannel over baby's shoulders to keep them warm. Pass the baby back to your partner when it is time to get them out. If you have older children, you can bathe baby with them too – see page 109 for more on bathing with siblings. As babies get older at about six weeks they will love a shower with you too. It is very stimulating for the senses so it could be activity time in the morning shower with mummy or daddy.

A Typical Day: One Week Old

Every baby is different, and in the early days it is more of a rhythm than a routine so take this as a very loose guide and adapt it to your own baby. Adjust the time you start your day depending on what happened in the night, and then continue three-hourly feeding. (Some babies may still want to feed a bit more often than this, so anywhere between 2-3 hours.) I advise changing the nappy halfway through to wake baby, but a bottle-fed baby will stop when they are ready and may not be as sleepy as a breastfed baby.

06:30

Feed, halfway through, change nappy. Give the rest of the feed. Burp, then swaddle and place back in basket to sleep. This will probably take up to an hour. You go back to sleep if you can.

09:30

Feed, halfway through, wash your baby's face to freshen up and change nappy, then give the rest of the feed, burp and swaddle and place back in basket to sleep or just cuddle and enjoy your baby.

12:30

Feed, then change halfway through, then give the rest of the feed. Burp and swaddle to sleep. Continue this sequence all day.

15:30

Feed and change.

18:30

Feed and change.

21:30

Feed, or if your baby is sleeping I would leave them until 22:30 (but no longer than four hours). You want the longest sleep whilst you are sleeping. Swaddle and settle for bed, and fingers crossed that you'll get four hours or more sleep.

If your baby is full-term and healthy, and has no medical issues, let them wake you. They will probably wake at approximately 01:30 to 02:00. Then 05:30 to 06:00.

Remember:

Be calm and confident.

Cuddling and feeding on demand will not spoil your baby.

Swaddling can help a newborn feel secure and sleep well.

Follow safe sleep guidelines.

Your baby is adjusting to life outside the womb – be patient.

"The connection Fiona has with babies is something I personally have never seen before. Sometimes when they look at one another it feels like they are having a conversation in entirely their own language."

Sophia, mother of Anastasia, Gabriel and Christina

Bonding

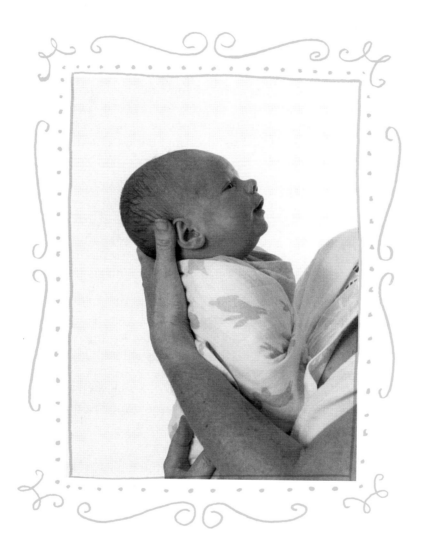

Brilliant baby massage, communication cues and precious first smiles.

You and Your Baby

Having a new baby is an exciting time, but it is really important that you look after yourself. I cannot stress this enough.

You are no good to anyone, including your baby, your partner or your family, if you are exhausted. Make sure you get rest when you can. Have a drink and a snack in the morning if you can't face breakfast then go back to sleep. If you don't have to start your day early then stay in bed. For the first few weeks, your baby will eat often but will sleep quite a lot so take this time to recover to the adjustment and excitement of having a new baby in the house.

Some women are on a complete high after their baby is born but this adrenaline soon wears off and you can suddenly feel very tired. Try to eat breakfast, lunch and dinner and a snack in between. Eat healthily, so you have lots of energy, but if you are craving sweet things, then have whatever your body is asking for. Remember to drink plenty of fluids too, to keep from getting dehydrated, as this itself can make you feel tired.

When your baby arrives you will have endless visitors. Everyone wants to see you and the new baby, but visitors can be very tiring so don't feel pressured to see everyone if you are not ready. Arrange visits when it is a good time for you – maybe when the baby is feeding so at least you are sitting, and both you and baby are awake. Also don't tire yourself by making lots of tea and biscuits; relax, show them where the kettle is and they can make you one. Your friends and family won't mind.

Accept help when it's offered.

Anyone who has had a baby knows how tiring it can be, so if someone offers to load the dishwasher or hang out the washing, then let them. They genuinely want to help. They would not offer if they didn't want to, and it's a few less things for you to think about. Allow your partner or family to help you keep on top of the housework but please don't stress about it. You and the baby are the important ones; the housework will still be there tomorrow and, if you do find time to do it, there will still be more housework tomorrow too!

So many times as a maternity nurse I have heard from new mothers 'I have not had time to shower' or 'the baby won't sleep'. Your baby doesn't need to be sleeping for you to take a shower or do something essential. Once your baby is fed and changed put them somewhere safe in a basket or bouncer chair and go and take a shower. Your baby won't go anywhere and, if they are unsettled, you can take them in the bathroom with you where at least you can still see them; babies love the sound of running water so they will probably be quite happy in there with you.

Let your baby get used to being in their basket awake. It's wonderful to give them cuddles, and we will look at the importance of touch on pages 62–63, but it is equally important that they gradually get used to being put down. You baby will look around then drop off to sleep, or may start to cry when getting tired, but will then go to sleep.

Do as much as you can whilst baby is awake; you don't have to be playing and entertaining your baby all the time. Watching you eat your breakfast is enough entertainment for your little one, then you can enjoy a rest or some time to yourself whilst they are sleeping. In fact, over-stimulation of your baby is a cause for a cranky baby. They get tired very quickly. Don't feel guilty for taking time to look after yourself – what's best for baby is best for you too, and vice versa.

A Note on Postnatal Depression (PND)

It's quite normal to feel a bit overwhelmed, tearful or anxious after giving birth. This is called the "baby blues" and is especially common on about day two to four after your baby is born, when your hormones are running wild. Once the first shock is over, most mothers find their emotions settle, although tiredness is a huge factor so it's important to rest as much as possible. For some mothers, though, postnatal depression can start at any point in the first year after giving birth, and may develop suddenly or gradually. There is an excellent guide on the NHS website, so if you are feeling persistent sadness, extreme tiredness or apathy, having trouble bonding or feeling that you're unable to look after your baby, or experiencing frightening thoughts, please don't suffer in silence. Look up the symptoms and get help. PND is very treatable and your GP or Health Visitor will get you the support you need.

How Babies Communicate

From the moment your baby is born they already recognise voices. A baby will turn to the voice of their mother if being held by someone else, and they will turn to the sound of their father too.

Your baby has been listening to your voices whilst in the womb for months so they are already familiar with the family around them. They know their mother's smell, and will be instantly calmed when held by her.

Babies love faces and will mimic your expression. If you sit with your newborn close to your face, approximately 12 inches away, they will watch you intently. If you frown, they will frown, if you poke your tongue out they will poke their tongue out! Be patient: you need to repeat what you are doing and they will slowly copy. Sometimes you might look away because you think they won't do it and then they do. Because babies love faces, they will watch with such concentration, really studying your face, which is why they find it so tiring. When they have had enough of looking at you, your baby will look away. This is a cue for you to stop talking to them; they need a little quiet time. Sometimes baby will look back at you and you can continue your interaction, but if you continue to try to interact and your baby doesn't want to, then your baby will start to cry.

Crying is communication; it is a baby's way of telling you they are hungry, bored, not interested any more or tired, or maybe just want to see a smiley face and interact; or it could be they need reassurance that you are there and they are not alone. Some babies cry very little and some babies cry a lot. This could just be down to their personality; we are all different. Some of us are quiet and some of us can be very loud. These are two extremes – most babies are somewhere in between. Unless there is an underlying cause for excessive crying, such as pain of some kind with a medical cause, then it is probably your baby's personality.

If your baby seems to cry more than some of your friends' babies, this is in no way a reflection on your parenting skills and it doesn't mean that they will always be difficult. Watching for your baby's cues is really helpful because you can anticipate what is going to set your baby off crying and try to change the situation to minimise this. Try to follow your baby's cues. This will make your life easier because you are listening to them as they tell you what they want.

Cues to watch for:

- **Crying when hungry.**
  When a baby is hungry, the cry will start off slow and quiet, and will become louder and louder and will not let up until baby is fed. Your baby will probably have already been showing other signs of hunger before crying, such as poking out their tongue or swiping their hands across their mouth.

- **Crying when tired.**
  A tired cry may start off loud but will tail off with a half-hearted, can't be bothered sort of cry.

- **Looking away.**
  If your baby looks away when you are talking, smiling or singing this means they have had enough. They are not interested any more. Sometimes they will also close their eyes almost like saying "I can't see you or hear you". They may take a little break then turn back to you for more communication or they may just cry if they have really had enough.

- **Yawning.**
  They are tired! This is a cue to put them in their bed to sleep. If you miss this cue your baby will cry because they are overtired.

- **Jerking their arms/waving them uncontrollably.**
  This is not your baby getting active or excited and playing, this is over-stimulation. Your baby will then cry and won't be able to fall asleep because the body has become over-active; often they are banging themselves in the face or touching the mouth, which causes the 'rooting reflex' when they aren't actually hungry. Try a swaddle (see pages 38–41).

- **Rubbing eyes/face.**
  When baby is approximately 7 to 9 weeks old, your baby will also rub their eyes or face when they are tired, and then cry if you missed it.

Different personalities

Some babies are not bothered at all by noise or movement and are completely chilled out, but some need things quieter and calmer; some babies will happily sleep at any time, some need to keep to a routine; some babies will just look around happily in their cot then drop off to sleep, and others will cry or shout at everything. We are all different; some people complain about almost everything and some are relaxed and take everything as it comes.

A more high-needs baby might cry at every nappy change, at bath time and might only stop shouting when their needs are met – such as being fed or put to bed – and even then they might need to shout to go to sleep. Remember, when this baby shouts to go to sleep, they are just saying 'Oh, I'm so tired I need to go to sleep and can't drop off' or 'Oh, I'm so tired and will eventually fall asleep'. If you pick this baby up constantly when they are crying and trying to go to sleep, it will take longer because the 'I'm trying to go to sleep' cry has been interrupted by you. Try to leave your baby – they will go to sleep on their own. If you were really tired, how would you feel if someone kept disturbing you?

A routine of some kind allows everybody, including your baby, to know what is happening.

You can be happy and confident that each day will be similar and you can plan around feed times, knowing what to expect from your baby and what to do next. Watching for your baby's 'cues' can help to minimise distress. Wriggling, grimacing, arching the back, yawning or turning away can be signs that baby needs to be left alone or be put in their basket. They may play and chat with themselves then go to sleep. If you missed the first yawns then baby will become tired and will cry.

If your baby doesn't like being naked, then keep a towel or blanket over them at bath time or nappy changes. This will help them to feel secure. Try imagining yourself in your baby's situation and how you might feel if the same were happening to you. If they are jerking their arms and hands then secure with a swaddle.

Interacting with Your Baby

Babies really are clever little beings! Have you noticed how your baby seems to hate having the vest over their head, especially if their eyes are covered? They will grimace and wriggle and if anything is left over their eyes they will cry, but they will also bring their hands towards their head and try to remove the object. If left long enough they would get it off their face, but please don't try this at home. The same thing happens when a hat falls over baby's eyes, they will wriggle until it's off and their face is clear again.

As mentioned above, babies love faces – talking to, singing to and reading to your baby from birth is crucial for them to develop.

Do as much staring at your baby and communicating as you like – it's all wonderful for both you and them.

Smiling

In my time as a maternity nurse to many babies, I have noticed that some babies smile very early, at approximately 2 to 3 weeks old. These babies will give direct eye contact and smile at you, but you have to be quick or you will miss it. Many people dismiss this as wind, because a baby with uncomfortable wind may have a twitchy face, but if baby has made eye contact I would say the smile at you is real. However as part of normal development a smile is not expected until approximately 6 to 8 weeks. At this age a baby's smile will last longer and become more obvious. As with all things to do with development, try not to worry if your baby does not appear to have smiled by 8 weeks. As you communicate more with your baby it will come. If you have concerns, do speak with your Health Visitor.

When babies are cooing and gurgling at you, try to make the same sounds back. They enjoy this. They think 'Wow, you really understand me, let's chat'.

Some babies at around seven to nine weeks will stop interacting with you, telling you they are ready to sleep. When you put them in their bed, they smile at you and become very chatty, as you have listened to them – they are saying 'thank you', that's just what they wanted. Some babies will need to cry themselves to sleep.

Babies love dark on light objects to look at. This is because their vision is still developing and dark on light is easier for them to see. They often look at pictures on a light wall or beams in a house. You can buy black and white cards or soft books for your baby to look at with you, or as a mobile as they lie in their cot or on a mat.

Baby Massage and the Importance of Touch

I believe you can never give too many cuddles or too much love. The more love and nurturing you can give, the more safe and secure your baby will feel and they will grow to be a confident and independent child.

Don't be concerned that you will spoil your baby, there is no such thing. When your baby is born they need to be close to you; they have been in your womb for nine months. Your baby will soon learn to sleep on their own in a cot. There is time for that, but in the first few weeks enjoy this time of closeness. Babies grow up too fast.

To encourage closeness, infant massage is a great way to communicate love through touch. When massaging your baby you also have close eye contact, which enables your baby to interact with you, however young.

The skin is the largest sensory organ in our bodies. Our body is covered with hundreds and thousands of sensory cells. When touched, the nerve cells start firing messages to the brain. This improves brain body communication, and any stimulation for your baby helps with brain development.

Research by Dr Tiffany Field on premature babies has found that when massaged daily, those babies spent more time in an active alert and awake state, cried less, had lower cortisol hormone levels (indicating less stress), and went to sleep faster after a massage than they did after rocking alone. Over a six-week period, the massaged babies gained more weight, had an improved emotional sociability and 'soothability' temperament, had decreased urinary stress hormones and increased levels of seratonin (one of the brain's natural pain relievers). These babies left the hospital earlier than those babies not massaged.

As a maternity nurse I found that, after bathing the baby, a natural thing to do was rub oil or a baby moisturiser into a baby's skin. I saw that babies loved this (think how nice your own skin feels when you have moisturised) and so I learned how to massage a baby properly through the IAIM (International Association of Infant Massage). I found the course truly amazing and inspirational. I learned how babies deprived of touch, such as those growing up in European orphanages in the 1980s, for example, do not develop well mentally or physically. Without loving touch, a baby or child cannot thrive.

Since doing the course I am now able to teach mothers and fathers to massage their baby, and watch them enjoy those moments. I encourage you to explore going along to an IAIM class. There you will meet other parents in the same situation as you and it is a wonderfully relaxing class for you and your baby.

I once worked with a family where I had taught the mother to massage her baby and suggested showing Dad how to massage. He was very busy and quite highly stressed – he needed to be this way for his job. I asked him a couple of evenings in a row, after baby had bathed, to come and massage his baby. He said 'yes' but was always busy. Then one evening he came into the bathroom ready to try. We sat on the floor, I had a doll, he had the baby and we started the massage. Baby was cooing and chatting to his father. It was amazing; I watched the stress disappear from this man, and he enjoyed this close communication that was happening between them as much as his baby did. A baby massage is of great value to fathers as well as mothers, particularly as they don't always have the same close time with their baby, especially when mum is breastfeeding.

Make time for this. It is a wonderful thing to do yet so simple.

Benefits of baby massage

- Helps neuron/brain development.

- Enhances communication with your baby through touch, eye contact and verbal responses between the two of you.

- Produces feel-good hormones for both you and your baby.

- Helps you bond with your baby, and can reduce postnatal depression.

- Reduces stress hormones, therefore helping your baby to cope better with reflux, wind and constipation.

- Improves stimulation levels, enabling your baby to cope with more stimulation before getting too tired or stressed.

- Relaxes your baby, helping them sleep.

How to massage your baby

Only massage your baby at a time that is good for your baby, so when they have just woken or when your baby has fed and is in a happy alert state. If your baby is tired or getting tired, then a massage would be too stimulating and your baby will get upset. Watch for your baby's cues – if your baby does not want a massage then respect this and give it at another time, but if your baby has had all their needs met, a full tummy, not too tired, then they will probably love it.

Begin with the legs and feet. Work your hands from the thigh to the foot. Not too firm, but don't tickle. Use a pulling motion to 'milk' the leg.

On the foot, stroke your thumbs from heel to toe in a thumb over thumb motion.

Use your index finger and thumb to roll on each toe from base to tip.

Use your thumb to press all over the base of the foot.

Using both thumbs, stroke from leg to toe.

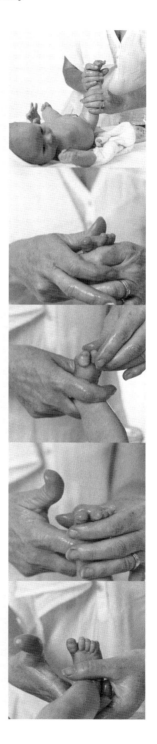

Create small circles with your thumbs around the ankle.

Hold the foot and give it a little bounce to let your baby know you have finished.

Repeat the same strokes on the other leg.

Next, massage the arms and hands. Work your hands from the top of the arm to the hand in a pulling motion. Then use your index finger and thumb to touch each finger from base to tip.

Stroke the top of the hand using both thumbs and massage the palm of the hand with your fingers. Repeat the same strokes on the other arm.

Rest your hand on the chest before any movements. Take your hand from the chest and stroke up over the shoulder, then cup the shoulder. Repeat for the other shoulder.

Turn baby onto their tummy and stroke their back with your fingers. Draw small circles all over the back with your fingertips. Gently rest your hands on the lower back to let them know you have finished. Cuddle them up to you in a towel or blanket.

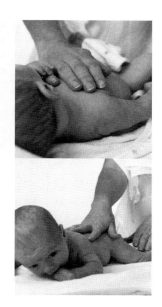

Massage is the giving and receiving of love and it doesn't cost a thing.

The Wonder of Water

Water has similar benefits to massage as it stimulates all the senses. I have taken babies for hydrotherapy as young as two weeks old. It is amazing how these little beings are so naturally relaxed in the water. The baby can be crying because you have just removed their clothes and nappy and as soon as the little float is placed under their chin and baby is placed in the water, peace and tranquility takes over. The baby goes into a unique meditative state. It is wonderful to see the parents watch in awe as babies freely floating in water behave in a way that you will not see at any other time. They are watched carefully by the therapist, and whilst some of the newborns go straight to sleep their senses are still being stimulated whilst in the water. If they start to show any signs of stress or of being over-tired, they are gently removed from the water, wrapped in a warm soft towel and cuddled or fed by mummy, they then enjoy a gentle massage and often leave the premises sleeping soundly in their pram. For more information, do visit www.yourbabyspa.com, founded by the lovely Laura Sevenus.

Bathing with your baby gives similar benefits to massage and hydrotherapy. You are cuddling and bonding with your baby. You are stimulating your baby's senses from the sound of the water, touch from you and the warm water on your baby's skin, the smell of your skin. Your baby may sleep on your chest with their body in the warm water, and even though baby is sleeping all of their senses are still being stimulated, which is good for neuron development and a wonderful thing for you as parents, creating special memories.

Remember:

Stimulate your baby's senses.

You can never give too many cuddles or too much love.

Look after yourself. Happy parents, happy baby.

Respond to your baby's cues. Every baby is different.

Make time for massage.

"Fiona is a great combination between structured and flexible. She never imposed her opinions or ways of doing things on us, but asked us what our goals were and offered suggestions, taking great interest in our babies' wellbeing. Fiona was able to ease both babies into a routine which allowed us all to get the rest we needed."

Jackie, mother of two very happy little babies

The First Two Weeks

Gently guiding your baby into a feeding and sleeping routine.

Your Baby Changes Every Day

For the first six weeks, expect things to change! Just when you think you have everything under control, and you have had the perfect routine for days, then it all seems to go wrong.

Don't worry, it hasn't! Your baby is probably hungry, or is just tired today. They are a little human being, after all, and won't function like a robot, so just go with the flow.

It doesn't matter if you have to move feeds a little because you have an appointment or need to be somewhere. Just adjust your day as you go. As long as your baby has eaten well between 06:00-07:00 and 23:00 then they should only need to feed once in the night.

Don't expect too much of your little one. You will have some sleepless nights for these first six weeks, but when you look at the big picture, six weeks out of your life is a very short period and this time with your baby is so precious because it goes by so fast and they will be changing in looks, gaining weight, and making little happy noises. So enjoy.

A Typical Day: Two Weeks Old

I have set out a typical day as a guide to follow. In the first two weeks your baby pretty much eats and sleeps, but by week three your baby is awake much more, then by week six, a routine is set which can stay in place for some time and you only need to cut back on the nap times. You can find all these routines together week-by-week on pages 127–141.

07:00
Feed, change halfway through, then feed. Burp, swaddle and settle. You sleep if you can.

10:00
Feed, change, finish feed. Burp, swaddle and settle (or your baby might be awake and want to look around for 10 minutes, then settle to sleep).

13:00
Feed, change, finish feed. Burp, swaddle and settle (or your baby might be awake and want to look around for 10 minutes, then settle to sleep).

16:00
Feed, then halfway through, give a bath, (see pages 48–50). Then finish feed and swaddle and settle in basket. Your baby will be very tired.

19:00
Leave until 19:30 if sleeping and wake for feed. Change, burp and finish feed, swaddle and settle in basket.

22:30
Feed, change, feed and straight back to sleep.

Now you go to bed too and hope for some sleep. Let your baby wake you.

Hopefully your baby will let you sleep until 02:30 if you're lucky. Feed, change, finish feed and burp. Settle to sleep.

Then 06:00 to 06:30 start your new day.

Breastfeeding

By the end of the first week your milk supply should be increasing every day and hopefully your confidence to feed your baby too. The length of time your baby needs to feed is very individual and you will find what works for you.

You need to feed for long enough that your baby settles and doesn't feed again for at least three hours from the start of that feed. Some babies will feed quickly, 15-20 minutes on one breast and be satisfied and others will feed up to 30 minutes on both breasts or a little longer. You will know baby is taking enough when they fall asleep and stay asleep for several hours before demanding more.

As a maternity nurse I advise mothers to let the baby feed for as long as they like (they normally fall asleep at the breast), then burp them, if needed, and change the nappy. This shifts any wind and wakes them up. They can then be offered the same breast if they haven't fed for long, let's say less than 20 minutes, or the other breast and they will feed some more and settle to sleep for longer.

To get your baby to sleep well, they need to eat well.

If you have fed your baby and they seem settled, but then wake and are hungry after an hour, feed for longer next time and wake them up whilst feeding. Make sure baby is feeding and swallowing and not just snoozing at the breast.

Some babies will feed for just a short time at the breast and sleep and feed four-hourly. Others will feed for over an hour and still need to feed two and a half to three-hourly; they are all different and it is all normal. If your baby seems to be feeding a lot, don't worry, they are only a week or two old and will get more efficient at feeding. As a baby grows their tummy grows too and can take bigger feeds and it does get easier. By week two your baby will have fallen into a pattern of three-hourly feeding, if feeding well.

It is quite common for some babies to feed a lot in the evenings. Again don't worry, they are just stimulating the breast to produce more milk; this will settle down. In my experience most babies want to just eat and sleep for the first two weeks. Enjoy this time for lots of cuddles and for you to rest when your baby is sleeping.

Supply and demand

When feeding your baby, think of it as supply and demand. The more your baby feeds, the more milk your breasts will make for your baby. In the early days your baby grows rapidly so their appetite increases constantly. There will be days when they are feeding more frequently or for longer but don't worry they are just making more milk, and they will settle down again when their appetite is satisfied. Some babies will feed more frequently for just 24 hours, others for longer, maybe 48 hours, but just let your baby feed. They are doing a good job at making more milk.

When your baby has been feeding you may notice that the inside of their lips go white and sometimes a little blister appears on the top lip. This is completely normal and is from the friction and the good suck of your baby.

Increasing milk supply with expressing

There may be a particular time of day when you think your breast milk may be low, for example if your baby is typically not settling from their 19:00 feed and seems hungry, then you can express after this feed for two days and your milk supply should increase and baby should then start to settle again. The same goes for any other time of day. Or you could express after every feed for two days and increase your supply.

Two steps forwards, one step back

You may be two and a half to three weeks in, your baby seems to be following their own routine of three-hourly feeds . . . and then suddenly it seems like it's all going wrong. Your baby is crying and hungry all the time. This is perfectly normal when breastfeeding!

Some babies want to feed a lot in the evenings or some just more frequently all day; some keep to a similar time but feed for longer. Because breastfeeding is supply and demand, your baby has to make more milk by suckling at the breast. They are growing very fast, gaining approximately 1oz/30g per day, so their appetite is increasing too. Your milk supply has to increase to satisfy the demand. The only way to do this is for more milk to be taken off the breast, so feed whenever it is needed. This increase in appetite usually lasts for approximately two days and everything calms back to normal. Just let your baby do the job of making more milk, even if it feels like you can't possibly have any left in there. They will then go back to their little routine, possibly for four or five days, then an increase in demand will return again, which is why it feels like two steps forwards and one step back, but slowly you will get there. Babies grow rapidly in the first months and all babies are different, but at three weeks and six weeks these growth spurts are very noticeable so bear with it. The increase in demand for milk only lasts a couple of days.

If you follow one of my flexible routines, baby will be doing the same thing roughly at the same time every day and will go down happily for naps and sleep times with no fuss. Your baby will know what is happening and know what to expect. A newborn baby is completely different from a 6-week-old baby so don't rush your newborn too much. Use these early days to get to know your baby. Hold them close, chat and learn your baby's language and 'cues' and learn to listen to what your baby is asking or telling you (see page 59).

Bottle-feeding

By the end of baby's second week I would expect them to be drinking 3oz/90mls of formula at every feed and feeding as often as three to four hours, and only waking once in the night at approximately 02:30 to 03:00.

This is an approximate guide as your baby may eat more or less in quantity and may drink more or fewer bottles per day depending on weight. Your baby will start with a 2 to 3-hourly schedule then progress to a 3.5-hourly schedule then possibly to 4-hourly.

Age	Number of feeds per 24 hours	How much for each feed
Birth to 2 weeks	6 to 8	Up to 90ml/ 3oz
2 to 4 weeks	5 to 6	Up to 120ml/4oz
4 to 8 weeks	5 to 6	Up to 150ml/5oz
8 to 12 weeks	5	180ml/6oz or more

Bottle-feeding with expressed breast milk

If you are expressing because you are giving the expressed milk in a bottle – for example, you are not comfortable with breastfeeding but you like the idea that your baby is having breast milk, or you can't breast feed because it is too uncomfortable or your baby doesn't suck well for whatever reason – then you should try to mimic the way a baby would naturally feed with your expressing sessions.

A breastfed baby would naturally feed anywhere between 2.5-hourly to 4-hourly feeds with little breaks whilst feeding, and would take a small amount of milk at one feed and large amount at another. So if you decide to express for say 15 minutes on each breast every 3 hours and stick to this rigidly, then your milk supply will not naturally increase.

For your milk supply to continuously increase you need to express a little bit randomly and not in a rigid routine.

So you could express 5 to 6 times a day, for example 07:00 then 10:00 which is 3 hours, then at 13:30, which is 3.5 hours, then 16:30, which is back to 3 hours, again between 19:30 and 20:00 which is 3 to 3.5 hours, then at 22:30. The next day you could allow a 4-hour gap between one feed and do a 2.5-hour gap somewhere else, also, vary the length of time you express so you could do 20 minutes on both breasts then the next one 40 minutes on both breasts, then 15 minutes on both breasts etc.

Take a little break of say 10 minutes when expressing because you would probably change your baby's nappy in the middle of a feed; also your milk will start to slow down so by taking a little break and going back to the same breast it will often allow some more milk to start flowing.

Keep a record of times, how long you expressed and how much milk you expressed, and try to get a little bit more each day because your baby's appetite will be increasing all the time as they grow.

Time	How long	How much
07:00	30mins left 30mins right	40mls 40mls
11:00	20mins left 20mins right	30mls 30mls
15:00	25mins left 25mins right	40mls 40mls
18:00	15mins left 15mins right	25mls 25mls
22:00	30mins left 30mins right	40mls 40mls
Use these times as an approximate guide	Adjust the duration slightly each day	Increase the amount every day

These amounts are estimates only; your baby may start off drinking tiny amounts e.g. 60–90mls, but by the time your baby is 2 weeks old they may be drinking 100mls at each feed. At 3 to 4 weeks, 110–120mls per feed. If you are giving expressed milk in a bottle and your baby is drinking it all, then increase it by 10mls, and keep increasing it each time they finish the new amount.

In my experience, and from seeing the amounts babies are drinking when giving expressed milk, they usually drink more in quantity than a formula-fed baby. So if you are looking at a formula guide, I would give at least 20–30mls more when giving breast milk. Only express during daytime hours; don't get yourself tired by expressing during the night. You should be sleeping when baby is sleeping.

Storage of milk

Once milk has been expressed put your milk straight into the fridge and store for 24 hours; if not used, put it in the freezer and use within three months. It will keep well if left out for a while because it has natural antibodies in the milk, but ideally you should store straight away. Label the milk with the date. Try to use the milk as soon as possible, as the properties in breastmilk keep changing to meet your baby's nutritional requirements as they grow.

Combination Feeding

As a maternity nurse I usually do the late evening feed and the night feeds. Some mums choose to express in the mornings, so I have milk to give the baby at night and they can go to bed early and rest. Some mums say to me at the start, I am only breastfeeding from 07:00 to 19:00, so then I give formula for the other feeds. There is no reason why you can't do the same if you are finding solely breastfeeding difficult. The baby doesn't get confused if they have a bottle then breast, in fact the earlier you give a bottle the better if you want to avoid nipple confusion. I have never had a newborn baby (under one month old) with nipple confusion; they instinctively know how to suck a bottle and how to milk the breast. If you exclusively feed your baby only from the breast for a month then your baby will not take a bottle easily, because they will have become used to the breast. The way a baby sucks from a bottle is very different from the breast, so introduce an expressed milk feed early to prevent a problem. However if you intend to breastfeed for a long time then your baby will never need a bottle so can go straight to a cup when weaning.

If you are combination feeding your body will adjust to how many feeds you are doing, your milk will still continue to increase in the daytime and you will be well rested. Obviously, if breastfeeding is working well for you then you will be finding it easy to feed in the night and drop off back to sleep, but if you are exhausted and thinking of giving up then try the combination feeding option. You will find you can continue breastfeeding for quite some time and your baby will soon give up the evening and night-time feeds, so they can continue on the breast in the daytime until weaning.

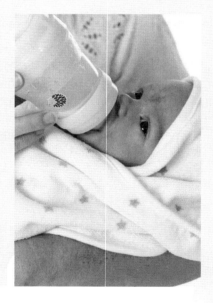

Colic, Wind and Other Feeding Issues

Colic

Colic is a word traditionally used to describe an irritable or unsettled baby, but today it is also used to define a condition where babies cry nonstop for seemingly no reason. Wind is also sometimes called colic and if that is the case, all babies have colic, because we know that they all need burping to bring up wind. It can be uncomfortable and for some babies very painful, so it's important to get wind up before your baby falls asleep or wind gets trapped and more difficult to shift.

Babies cry for lots of reasons, so seemingly 'non-stop' crying could be a number of different things. Your baby could be hungry, and in the very early days most crying is because of hunger. It may seem like they have only just fed, but they are ready for some more. Tiredness is also a reason for crying and this is the most difficult for parents to deal with because they have fed the baby, burped well, had a little chat with mum, dad, grandparents etc., and are now ready to be put down to settle to sleep. Baby lies there for a few minutes then starts crying. So of course they are picked up. If baby is only crying because they are tired, and then they are constantly picked up, they can't go off to sleep. Some babies need to be left to cry themselves to sleep. Some will turn it into a scream and just stop suddenly to sleep.

This sort of crying confuses parents. They think something is wrong, when most of the time the baby is saying 'I am really tired and I can't get to sleep'. If your baby is crying and throwing their arms in the air, punching the air or just jerking their arms about, then I would swaddle the baby and put them back in their cot and they will cry to sleep. If they are an older baby, over six weeks, then your baby may be so tired and over-stimulated that they can't go to sleep, so will need to be put somewhere quiet, as any noise will jerk them awake or be irritating. An over-stimulated baby will scream and it is natural to think they are in pain when they may just be very tired.

If you are relaxed and go to bed you generally sleep well and will drop off easily to sleep, but if you are tired or stressed about something your mind can't shut off. You become more irritable and more tired and can't get to sleep. You need to have silence because anything irritates you. Babies are the same.

Some babies may need to be swaddled and then calmed in your arms for a few minutes, but I always like to put them in the cot slightly awake, so the baby knows where they are. If you let them fall asleep on you and then place them in the cot, they are going to wake up wondering where they are and how did they get there. Baby was in a soft warm place, all cuddled up, close to someone, and now they are gone, so it is natural baby will cry. Settle baby in your arms by all means, and when they are looking dozy but not quite asleep, put them in their cot. That way baby will go off to sleep and sleep well, knowing where they are.

Obviously if you think your baby cries excessively or doesn't eat well and is not gaining weight or brings their knees up and seems to be in pain, there could be a medical problem e.g reflux, silent reflux, lactose intolerance or something else, so consult your GP.

Reflux

Some reflux, as in spitting back milk, can be normal. This is called a posit. Some babies will burp and bring back what seems quite a lot of milk; this is normal too. The valve or muscle between the oesophagus and the stomach is weak in newborn babies and if they eat excessively, which they mostly do, and the stomach is full, the valve will open and the milk will spill back out of the stomach, up the oesophagus and out through the mouth. This can be quite alarming if it is a lot of milk, but if your baby is happy and is gaining weight, then it is probably nothing to worry about. Obviously mention this to your GP if you are worried.

However, if your baby is vomiting at most feeds and it is projectile vomit, or if they are crying excessively and cannot be put down flat in a cot because milk spills up and out of the mouth or nose, this is reflux and there may be an underlying cause. See your GP.

Silent reflux

If your baby struggles to feed, only takes small amounts, cries excessively, screams a lot and arches or straightens their back, cannot be put down flat, is not gaining weight or is slow to gain weight, and is not vomiting or spilling back milk, then this is silent reflux.

Silent reflux is when the milk baby is able to eat stays in the stomach but the acid that is produced in the stomach to break down the milk spills back up the oesophagus. This burns the oesophagus and causes pain. Your baby will not be able to lie flat as the acid will spill back up.

For both reflux and silent reflux you can raise the head end of your baby's bed so the stomach contents stay down. It is probably similar to what we call heartburn, which is very uncomfortable.

For reflux and silent reflux, you must see your GP so you can be prescribed the correct medication to reduce acid production or to neutralise the acid. There may also be an underlying problem e.g. weaker than usual valve to the stomach, lactose intolerance or cow's milk protein allergy. Your GP can prescribe hypo-allergenic milk formula (if it is the milk that is causing the problem), or if you are breastfeeding you may need to change your diet.

If for any reason you think your baby is unwell or something is not normal, see your GP.

Breastfeeding Problems

Hopefully you are enjoying breastfeeding your baby, but it doesn't always come without problems. Here are a few that you might experience:

Engorgement

When you first start feeding, your breasts may become very full, hard and uncomfortable, but they will settle down. Your baby has probably been feeding a lot and it has caused your breasts to make more milk than is needed. Once your baby settles into a feeding pattern of two to three hours, your breasts will soften and settle down. To ease discomfort you could hand-express a tiny bit of milk off your breast, just to make yourself comfortable. If you express too much with a pump, you will make the problem worse because you will be telling your breasts to produce more and more milk. If your breasts are too full the baby will find it hard to latch on, so if you hand-express a tiny bit to soften around the areola, your baby will be able to latch. You can try putting hot or cold flannels on too. This can be comforting. There is also the old-fashioned remedy of cabbage leaves from the fridge – crush the stalks to release the juice (they don't smell very nice but it does ease the pain). Continue to feed and it will ease off.

Sore, cracked nipples and thrush

If your baby is not properly latched on to your breast then there will be lots of friction on your nipples. They will be cracked and sore and may even bleed. This can also cause engorgement because your baby isn't emptying your breast properly.

Make sure your baby is latched onto the breast, not the nipple. Your baby's mouth should open wide and be well onto the breast so the nipple goes right to the back of baby's mouth; it should not be painful if baby is on properly. Your baby's lips should be curled out (see page 28).

If you are sore, use lots of moisturising cream after every feed. If it is too painful you can try nipple shields. These will give your nipples a rest. Try them for 48 hours and you should be able to go back to feeding without them.

If you have been feeding with no nipple problems and then develop sore pink nipples with a burning pain after feeding, this may be a sign of thrush, a fungal infection. Get this checked by your midwife or GP. You may need anti-fungal medication. If you have thrush on your breast you may have transferred it to your baby, so check inside your baby's mouth for white patches on the inside of cheeks and the edge of the tongue. Obviously the tongue will be white from milk, so marks on the cheeks could be more of an indication. Also the other way round – if your baby has oral thrush then they may have transferred it to your breast.

Flat nipples or inverted nipples

You can still feed your baby with flat or inverted nipples although it may be a little difficult to get a good latch. Try pulling your nipple out and squeezing a little milk for baby to try to latch on to. If you are finding it really difficult, nipple shields work well. Once baby is on and has pulled your nipple out, slip the shield off and latch baby on again or, if it's easier, continue with the shield. I have seen women who have tried them as a temporary measure and continued to feed baby with them just fine. If it works for you, use it. If it seems impossible to get your baby on and you want your baby to have breast milk, you can always express it and give it in the bottle.

Tongue tie

Tongue tie is when the frenulum, the strip of skin which anchors the tongue, is too tight. It is anchored under the tongue and can be at the back (posterior) or towards the front (anterior). This can restrict the movement of the tongue. Not all babies with tongue tie have problems. If your baby is struggling to latch onto the breast or a teat and cannot suck without taking in air and causing wind, or if you are breastfeeding and it is particularly painful and you are suffering with sore cracked nipples, then you should have your baby's latch checked by a midwife or lactation consultant. If they suspect a tongue tie and it is causing problems they may consider referral to have the tie released by a specialist.

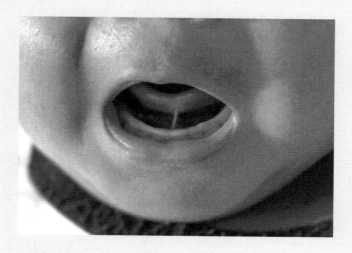

Mastitis

Mastitis is a blocked milk duct caused when breastmilk has not been draining efficiently and has become stationary in a duct. If you have mastitis you will probably feel unwell. If you have a headache or fever above 38°C, or both, along with a hot red patch on your breast, then you should see your GP as you may need antibiotics. It is very important that you continue to feed your baby; you must continue to let the baby drain the breast or it could turn into a more serious blockage of the duct and become a very painful abscess and need to be drained by a medical professional.

Try massaging your breast with the palm of your hand working from the chest towards the nipple to try to unblock the duct and get your milk flowing. You can do this whilst your baby is feeding. It will be uncomfortable, but persevere. You can also try warm flannels for comfort. To prevent occurrences, wear a good fitting bra as pressure from your bra can cause a blockage.

Remember:

Take your time.
Every baby is different.
Slowly guide them and it will
all happen soon enough.

Try not to listen to what
everybody else's baby is doing.
Do what you want to do; this
is your baby.

Get help with
breastfeeding
problems.

Try combination
feeding if you are
struggling.

"Fiona's attitude to routine is respectful of the baby, as she is firm in certain elements but also provides a little flexibility in the right places, to take into account each baby's mood and character."

Sophia, mother of Anastasia, Gabriel and Christina

The First Two Months

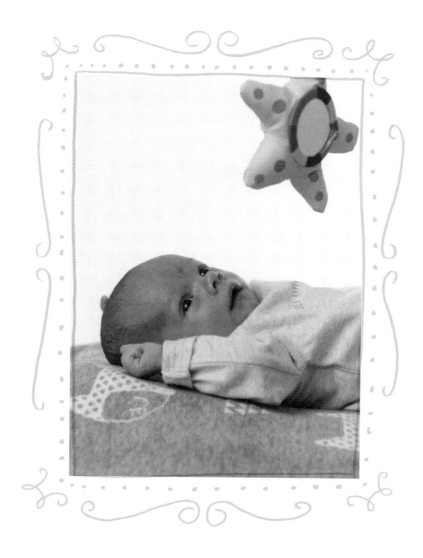

*Structuring your days and helping
your baby sleep longer at night.*

Realistic Routines

By three weeks, your baby is uncurling, becoming more awake and getting louder.

They will be awake to feed and will stay awake for a little while before showing signs of wanting to go to sleep. You can start to really make a difference between daytime and night-time and build in some more activity time as they get older. There are some flexible routines to follow at the end of the section but first let's look at different parts of your baby's day.

Activity and Awake Time

When your baby is first born there is no activity time. The time your baby is awake to feed is it! So baby may wake up, cry for food, take half an hour to an hour to feed, then go straight back to sleep. Your baby will eat and sleep around the clock.

As the weeks go by, your baby will be more awake during feeding and will stay awake for a little chat for, say, 20 minutes afterwards. You may feed then put your baby back in the crib and they will happily look around, then either cry because they are tired or drop off quietly to sleep. By week three baby will have 'uncurled' and be happy to look around. Try putting them in a chair or under a baby gym, or tuck a black and white book in the crib to look at. Their attention span will not last very long. Some babies may gaze at something for only 10 minutes and others will be entertained for longer. If your baby is still wide awake, not yawning or showing signs of tiredness, but cries, they may be bored, so move them or give them something else to look at. It may be they want a chat with you or a cuddle before going to sleep.

As your baby approaches one month to six weeks old, they will certainly want to spend much longer awake, so place them on the baby gym or under a mobile, and leave them to concentrate. You don't have to be the entertainer. I have watched many times a baby lying on their mat very contentedly, then mum or dad comes in and starts chatting excitedly or shaking toys in their face and the baby starts to cry. If this happens, it is because your baby is concentrating and you have created a disturbance.

Would you like it if you were reading the paper or a book and concentrating hard then someone came along and interrupted you or started shaking your book? You have to try to think like a baby. Before you know it your baby will be waking, eating, playing and then sleeping again at roughly the same times every day; you will have a nice routine in place and your baby will be very happy.

Activity Time

At this age, babies will just enjoy your attention and being talked to and involved in your life, but if you like to have some structure to your activity time, you can try any of the following:

- Sharing books

- Singing

- Walking around the house or garden

- A walk in the pram or sling outside

- Massage, or a bath or shower with you

- Sitting in a bouncy chair with toys on a bar

- Lying under a play gym or hanging mobile

Tummy time

During awake time or playtime it is important to give some tummy time, even if it is just a minute each day. At first your baby may not like this but if you do it regularly your baby will learn to bring their hands forward and lift their head. This is good for strengthening the neck and back muscles, and as they get used to it, your baby will be happy to lie on their tummy, bringing their head up and looking around to get a different view. Position yourself where baby can still see your face; they may not like it if they can't see anyone or anything. You could also place a mirror for baby to see the reflection.

Bedtime

Establishing a short bedtime routine is a good habit to get into – it doesn't have to be elaborate, it can just be as simple as a nappy change, wash and a massage, then a feed in a darkened room. The sooner your baby starts to distinguish between day and night, the quicker they will slip into a routine. Don't disturb your baby too much during night feeds. Don't change a nappy unless there is a poo. Keep the lights low and try not to chat to your baby. And establish a sleepy feed to naturally stretch their sleeping into the night-time hours.

The Sleepy Feed

In the early days, if your baby was last fed between 18:00–19:00, I recommend lifting your baby at 22:00. Your baby will be feeding anything from 2.5 hours to 4 hours in the day. You would ideally want the longest sleep to be in the night-time so I recommend lifting baby at 22:00 even if they are sleeping. You or your partner can feed and settle, and then everyone can go to sleep hopefully having had at least four hours before the next feed.

I never let a baby go longer than four-hourly feeding during the daytime hours between 07:00 and 23:00. All babies will naturally sleep for one long period of four to five hours during a 24-hour period, and ideally you want this to happen whilst you are sleeping in the night. If you let your baby sleep a long time in the daytime hours then your baby will wake at night, probably three-hourly, and you will not have a good night's sleep, resulting in you being tired during the day.

Allowing your baby to sleep later in the evening does not necessarily mean your baby will wake later in the night – they may still wake from habit but you will have missed out on a long stretch of sleep. For example, you have been feeding your baby at 22:00 for a couple of nights and they sleep until 03:00. So you think 'OK, tonight I am going to feed them a bit later, say, 23:00, and so they will sleep until 04:00', but no – they still wake at 03:00! So you have lost sleep by going to bed later and your baby still woke at the same time.

Once you have established the daytime routine and the sleepy feed at 10pm-ish, your baby will generally wake at the same time every night for a week or so. This is easier to cope with than your baby waking at random times because your body gets used to it. They will then start waking at 03:15, then 03:30, then might surprise you with a 04:00 wake up, then go back to 03:00 for a couple of nights. However, before you know it, two weeks will have passed and baby is now waking at 04:30, then 05:00 and will continue to progress through the night until they get to 07:00. Hooray, an all-night sleep!

As a maternity nurse, I find the majority of babies are sleeping from 22:00 until 07:00 by the age of 6 to 10 weeks if they are feeding well in the daytime hours, but don't worry if your baby isn't doing this, they will eventually. Be patient: baby needs to be 10lbs (4.5kg) or over in weight to be able to cope a long time without food. All babies learn to sleep through in their own time, and if they were smaller at birth it might take them a little longer. If, at six weeks old, your baby is still waking early, or needing two feeds in the night, then they are not getting enough food in the daytime hours and you might want to look at your routine again to up the milk intake.

What if my baby is too sleepy for the sleepy feed?

Sometimes your baby goes into such a deep sleep at around 22:00 that it is impossible to get them to feed, so what I would recommend is to try feeding half an hour earlier, before they have entered deep sleep. That way they will feed and you can get to bed early! Listen to your baby whilst they are sleeping; if at about 21:30 they are still making little noises, then you know they are not in a deep sleep and will feed, but once there is silence, that's when it is difficult to feed them. After a couple of nights of 21:30 you should be able to go back to 22:00-ish.

What if my baby won't take the sleepy feed or it makes no difference?

Some babies just won't do the sleepy feed; either they are too sleepy or it just doesn't make any difference. If when they are settled at 19:00 and are too sleepy when you lift them at 22:00, and you have tried doing it earlier and later than 22:00, then leave your baby to see how long they will sleep. If they usually wake around 03:00 having had the sleepy feed, then you leave out the sleepy feed and baby still wakes at 03:00, then you might as well forget it! Put them to bed at 19:00 as usual, have a nice quiet evening and go to bed early, (or get a babysitter and go out as you don't have to rush back for the sleepy feed). Hopefully, your baby will continue to progress through the night until sleeping 12 hours. Good luck!

Noises in the night

In my experience most babies make noises at night when they are sleeping. Some babies sleep very quietly and soundly until it's nearly time to feed, then they grunt and wriggle and can be quite loud but when you check them they are still asleep. So what I recommend is, don't go to them too soon. It might be another hour or so before they wake and actually cry for food. The longer your baby can go through the night until he feeds, the more likely he will then make it to 07:00 only feeding once in the night. Other babies will wriggle and squirm and grunt all night long, so you have to learn not to react to this and only listen out for the cry or else you will never get any sleep. So go to sleep, ignore the noises and wake up when they cry out through hunger and then feed them.

Typical Days: Week 3 Onwards

At this age, babies start to show their preferences, so I have suggested three possible options for you – try them to see what your baby likes best. Adjust the first feed time to suit you – you may want to start at 07:00 or 08:00 – and then feed every three hours.

Once your baby has fed, let them look around for a little while depending on how long they have been awake. Then put them back in their basket awake so they will learn to self-settle.

You don't have to get up yourself at the first feed time of the day; you and your baby can always go back to bed after the morning feed and get a bit more sleep in.

Week 3: Option 1

07:30

Feed, change, finish feed and let your baby stay awake, looking around under a mobile or baby gym. Your baby should not be awake longer than an hour and a half from start of feed. They will get very tired.

09:00

Swaddle and settle back to sleep.

10:30

Feed, change, finish feed, burp, and let your baby stay awake for a while.

12.00

Swaddle and settle to sleep.

13:30

Feed, stay awake no longer than an hour and a half.

15:00

Swaddle and settle to sleep.

16:30

Feed, stay awake.

18:00

Burp, swaddle and settle to sleep for 45 minutes. This is a power nap just to get them through to bath and bedtime.

18:45

Wake baby, give a bath and massage then feed, at 19:30 if baby can last until then, or feed anytime after 19:00 if baby is shouting for food. Burp, finish feed and settle straight to sleep.

22:30

Feed, change, finish feed, burp, swaddle, and straight back to sleep. All to bed and fingers crossed for some sleep.

Hopefully, wake at approximately 02:30 to 03:00, feed and settle straight back to sleep. Then get through to 07:30 – fingers crossed.

Week 3: Option 2

07:00
Feed, change, finish feed and let your baby stay awake, looking around under a mobile or baby gym. Your baby should not be awake longer than an hour and a half from start of feed or they will get over-tired.

08:30
Swaddle and settle back to sleep.

10:00
Feed, change, finish feed, burp, and let your baby stay awake for a while.

11:30
Swaddle, burp and settle to sleep.

13:00
Feed, stay awake no longer than an hour and a half.

14:30
Swaddle, settle and sleep.

16:00
Feed, stay awake.

17:30
Burp, swaddle and settle to sleep for 45 minutes. This is a power nap just to get them through to bath and bedtime.

18:45
Wake baby, give a bath and massage then feed, burp, finish feed and settle straight to sleep.

22:30
Feed, change, finish feed, burp, swaddle, and straight back to sleep. All to bed and fingers crossed for some sleep.

Hopefully, wake at approximately 02:30 to 03:00, feed and settle straight back to sleep. Then get through to 07:00 – fingers crossed.

Week 3: Option 3

If your baby is showing signs of tiredness e.g. yawning or crying, put them to sleep before the times mentioned.

07:00
Feed, change, finish feed then let your baby stay awake looking around under a mobile or baby gym. Your baby should be awake no longer than an hour and a half from start of feed. They will get very tired.

08:30
Swaddle and settle back to sleep. Some babies may take a while to fall asleep but should be asleep by 09:00 at latest or they will get over-tired.

10:30
If you've been waking your baby for this feed at 3 hours (10:00), you could try 3.5 hours from last feed (10:30). Feed, change, finish feed, burp and let your baby stay awake for a while.

12:00
Swaddle, burp and settle to sleep.

14:30 (4 hours from last feed)
Feed, stay awake no longer than an hour and a half.

16:00
Swaddle, settle and sleep.

17:00 (2.5 hours from last feed)
Small feed, stay awake.

17:45
Play, gym or chair.

18:45 (1.5 hours from last feed, to stock up for bedtime)
Bath and massage, then feed, burp, finish feed and settle straight to sleep. i.e. baby will have had more than one full feed but less than two.

22:00

Feed, change, finish feed, burp, swaddle and straight back to sleep. All to bed and fingers crossed for some sleep. Only change nappy if it has poo in it.

Hopefully wake at approximately 02:30 to 03:00, feed and settle straight back to sleep. Then get through to 07:00.

Week 4

At this stage I start to get a little bit strict about waking times. Your baby should be able to be awake for about 1 hour 30 minutes to 1 hour 45 mins at each waking time. I also adjust the feed times. However it is trial and error, so if it doesn't work and your baby wakes up in the evening or is awake in the night, then go back to three-hourly. Again, adjust your start time and work around it to fit in appointments that you need to keep.

07:00

Feed as usual, burp, nappy change, give rest of feed, then on play gym. Your baby should be ready to sleep after an hour and a half of being awake.

08:30

Settle to sleep. Baby should sleep for an hour and a half.

10.00

Feed as usual, burp, nappy change, give rest of feed then awake/activity.

11.30

Settle to bed in the quiet. If your baby is content and satisfied with food they will lie happily looking around then fall asleep. If baby has been lying happily, then you know they are not hungry. They may start to cry a little when tired but just leave them and they will go to sleep. Hopefully they will sleep for 2 hours. If baby can manage 2 hours then feed at 14:00, but feed anywhere between 13:00 and 14:00.

14:00

Feed as usual, burp, nappy change, give rest of feed, then on play gym or chair, or just a chat with you or friends.

15:30

Settle to sleep. Baby should sleep for an hour and a half.

17:00

Feed on breast or half a bottle and burp – give a small feed.

18:00

Give a nice relaxing bath, followed by a massage.

18:30

Give other breast or rest of the bottle then settle to sleep.

19:00

Asleep in bed for the evening.

22:00

Give a very sleepy feed, try not to disturb baby too much. Lift them from the cot, arouse them just enough to get them to feed. Let them feed for as long as possible, burp gently and place back to sleep. Only change the nappy if it has a poo in it.

Then off to bed and hope baby sleeps past 02:00 to 02:30. Your baby will probably be managing four or five hours from 22:00 by now but don't worry if not, it will come.

Week 5

Your baby should be able to stay awake for 2 hours now; try to get them to do one 3.5 or 4-hour session between feeds from 10:00 to 14:00, or from 10:30 to 14:30. If you are formula feeding or combined feeding, baby now needs to eat approximately 120ml to 150ml per feed, depending on weight (based on an average 10lb baby).

07:00
Feed as usual, burp, nappy change, give rest of feed then on play gym or chair. Your baby should be ready to sleep after 2 hours; try to keep them awake. This will make a difference to their night-time sleeping.

09:00 – 10:00
Sleep for up to one hour. Your baby will probably wake after half an hour but if they are sleeping wake up at 10:00.

10:30
Feed – this is stretching to three and a half hours. Then awake time. Play gym, bouncy chair or under mobile. Look out for tired cues after one and a half hours.

12:00 – 14:30
Sleep – baby should sleep well here, up to two and a half hours. If they haven't woken, wake at 14:30.

14:30
Feed, burp, change, awake time etc. Try to keep your baby awake until 16:30.

16:30 – 17:30
Sleep.

17:30
Awake. Gym or naked time in bathroom on mat on the floor.

18:00
Bath and massage followed by a feed.

Keep awake whilst feeding, burp well then into bed for 19:00.

22:00

Lift for sleepy feed. Then fingers crossed for a good night.

Week 6

Your baby should be awake for two hours at a time now. You are now trying to stretch your baby's feeds to 3.5–4 hours. The baby may manage three and a half in the morning then four hours over lunch, then three to three and a half in the afternoon until the early evening feed. Continue this routine for a month or longer; it depends if your baby is ready. If you have a routine that is working and your baby is sleeping well at night then don't change it unnecessarily.

07:00

Feed as usual, burp, nappy change, give rest of feed then on play gym or chair. Your baby should be ready to sleep after two hours. Try to keep them awake; this will make a difference to their night-time sleeping.

09:00 – 10:00

Sleep for one hour; your baby will probably wake after half an hour but if they are sleeping, wake them up at 10:00.

10:30 – 11:00

Feed – this is now stretching to four hours. Only do this if baby is able to. Obviously if they are crying and can't be consoled with playing or distraction then feed at 10:30.Then awake time (e.g. gym chair under mobile).

12:00 – 14:30

Sleep. Baby should sleep well here, up to two and a half hours. If they have not woken, wake at 14:30.

14:30 – 15:00

Depending if baby fed at 10:30 or 11:00, feed, burp, change, awake time etc. Try to keep them awake until 16:30.

16:30

Sleep for half an hour (longer if needed).

17:00 – 17:30
Awake. Gym or naked time in bathroom on mat on the floor.

18:00
Bath and massage followed by a feed; burp well then into bed for 19:00.

22:00
Lift for sleepy feed. Then fingers crossed for a good night.

Weeks 7 to 12

You can follow the routine above for a six-week-old right up until weaning at five to six months. By 10 to 12 weeks your baby should manage a four-hourly routine between feeds, but don't worry if your baby hasn't got to this stage yet and just continue with the three to three and a half hour routine, with a four-hour gap at midday. Again your baby may be starting his/her day at a different time, so adjust this to suit you. For an older baby, you will only need to cut back on nap times to make the routine work. By three months your baby should only need a 15-30min nap in the morning, 2 hours at lunch time and 15 minutes in the late afternoon, but if your baby is grumpy and needs more sleep then let them sleep a bit longer. Just make little adjustments and find what works.

Remember:

Make day and night different.

Babies need to be 4.5kg (10lbs) to go a longer stretch without food.

Make little adjustments not big changes.

Introduce a sleepy feed.

Have patience.

"I have been very lucky to have Fiona as a maternity nurse for both of my boys. Both slept through the night at an early stage although they both had very different paths to get there. Fiona was sure to find out what worked for each of them."

Delphine, mother of William, Alexander and Constance

Your Family and Other Animals

Introducing siblings, managing multiple births and preparing pets for change.

Siblings

Having a new baby in the family is a big change for everyone in the household. Here are some tips on making sure this time is relaxed for everyone.

If this is your second baby (or third, or more!), you will need to tell your existing children you are expecting a baby. The age of your child will depend on when and how you tell them. I don't advise telling them too early, as the time to wait for the baby will be too long and if your baby bump is not very big, younger children may not understand.

If your child is under about two and a half years old, they will adjust quite easily to a new baby. They may demand your time a little more, but after a week or so it will be like the baby has always been there. If your child is a little older, they will be able to understand what is happening but may not adjust as easily, as they have always had their parents to themselves and may find it difficult to share their time with the baby. Keep them informed and involved and it will be a normal progression for your family.

Before the birth

When your bump is visible it will be easier to explain. Tell your child that you are having a baby. Explain that it is inside your tummy and let them put their hands and ears on your bump to try to listen and feel your baby. It is far easier to understand if they can see something happening to your body. Tell them the baby is inside you and will be coming out soon. If your child has some little friends who already have brothers or sisters this will be easier for them to understand.

There are children's books you can buy where the story is about the arrival of a new baby brother or sister, and reading these stories will help prepare for the baby too. Get your child involved as much as possible with the preparation of the nursery, getting the crib ready and preparing the pram, baby clothes etc.

When your baby is due, have arrangements in place as to who is caring for your child, maybe they can stay with grandparents or someone they love can stay at your house. Try to keep things normal and try not to fuss and worry too much. Your child will adjust just fine. They have to, you can't send the baby back!

When your baby is ready to be born it is important you tell your child what is happening; that the baby is ready to be born and come out of your tummy. If you are going to hospital, explain where you are going and that you may be there for a few days but as soon as the baby is born, they can come and see you and the baby. I feel that for them to come and see you at the hospital with the new baby is important. It gives your child the chance to meet their new baby brother or sister and then they go home with Daddy, leaving you and baby behind. The older child then is able to chat with Daddy about it and is able to process what is happening before you come home with the baby. Without this it can be quite a shock for Mum to disappear and come back with this new baby when they weren't expecting it!

Don't hide things from your child. It is a big shock to little ones when they don't know what is happening. Even if your child is still very young, explain everything; you will be surprised at how well they will cope with all this information.

Some parents buy a little gift for the older child from the new baby. This is a positive thing about the new baby coming. You can also get a baby doll and crib for them to play with beforehand and show them pretend nappy changing and feeding, and how we are gentle with a baby.

Coming home with your baby

Once your baby is home try to keep things as normal as you can. Leave baby to sleep and tend to your older child. When baby needs to feed let the sibling watch closely. Explain what is happening, let them help when nappy changing, get them to fetch things or pass things to you and let them hold the baby if they want to. You can read stories to your elder child whilst you are feeding the baby. Have them play with puzzles close to you. Keep them informed and involved, and they will soon forget what it was like before the baby arrived.

The second child is very different from the first. You will find that your eldest child takes up most of your time and the baby just slots in.

Sit your older child safely on the couch or bed and place baby on their lap. They will put their arms around them, tell them to be gentle. Once they have held them for a very short time they will push baby back to you and will have had enough. As long as you don't push the older child out and say 'don't do this', 'don't do that' and make it fun and positive for them to have a brother or sister, they will accept it. Remember to teach the older child to be gentle and caring with the baby.

Never leave your older child alone with your baby at first, as you are not sure how they will react around them. Children can forget and be quite rough and there could be some jealousy issues, so if you leave them together in the room, it shows that you trust the older child, but watch them from the door so you can see how your older child is with the baby when they think you're not around. Some children will carry on playing with their toys, oblivious to the new baby. Another child will take any opportunity to bang baby on the head with a favourite toy, so be careful and aware that this can happen.

Keep things normal. Don't over compensate your time for the older child. They have to accept you have to sometimes feed and change baby and that baby is here to stay.

Remember:

If you are honest and talk to your child and answer questions appropriately for their age in a way that they understand, there shouldn't be any problems. They will love having a little baby brother or sister.

Bathing baby with siblings

You already have yourself organised for bathing your older child, so now you have a baby to bathe too. Why not bathe baby with your older child or toddler in the big bath? They will usually love sharing a bath with their younger baby brother or sister.

Prepare the bath safely, putting cold water in first then hot to a temperature of 36.5°C to 37.5°C. Don't add any bath products at this stage. You can add them for your older child after baby has got out. Have everything you will need in the bathroom with you. Baby can lie on the floor dressed or naked, if they like to be naked, and can listen to the water running. Put your older child in the bath first and start playing, but keep things quiet as baby is going to get in once your older child is happy to sit in the bath and play with toys, bottles, sponges etc. Place baby in the bath by lifting with one hand under the head and one under the bottom, then you can move baby's head onto your wrist and hold baby's arm with your fingers, so baby feels safe and secure. Wash baby with your free hand from head to toe then take baby out. Place on the towel you have ready and dry, massage and dress. Leave baby on a dry towel whilst you play and bathe the older child, then get them out of the bath and dry and dress. Both siblings happy and washed!

Twins and Multiple Births

With twins, triplets or multiple babies you have to be extremely organised or you will never have any time to yourself.

If you allowed the babies to do their own thing, one would wake up and feed – it may take an hour or so to feed and settle – and then another one would wake. By the time you have fed and settled the second baby, it will be time to feed another one and on it would go. In the following section I have focused on twins, but you can apply these principles to multiples too.

Feeding and routine

When one baby wakes, start to feed them and then when they seem happy, put them somewhere safe e.g. cot, crib or bouncer chair. Then wake the other baby and start to feed. When that baby is also settled, place them somewhere safe and change the first twin, finish feeding and settle them in the chair again, or if sleepy put to bed, then change the second one's nappy, finish feeding and settle to sleep. This way they are always awake at the same time, maybe 20 minutes apart, and always sleeping at the same time. So you get a break.

The other option is when one wakes, wake the other one too and feed them together. You can prop them up on pillows and breastfeed them together, or you can sit them in a chair and bottle-feed them at the same time. When they are both settled, burp and change nappies, then finish feeding and settle back to bed together.

If you go for the first option, realise that there will always be times when you have to feed together as they will both sometimes wake hungry at the same time. It's surprising how you learn to handle two babies at the same time. Usually with twins, one is patient and one is more demanding, so that helps. The more demanding twin always jumps the queue and the patient one allows it and doesn't care.

Follow the same routines that I have put in place for single babies (see pages 127–141), feeding the babies together or parting them by 20 minutes to half an hour as above.

Sleeping

If you are using moses baskets, you can let the babies sleep together in the daytime but I would separate them at night. If you have them sleeping in a big cot however, they can share this from birth until they are too big or moving around too much. Your babies have been together for nine months and they like the closeness. When they are tiny, you can place them side by side. As they grow, you can put them at opposite ends with their feet at the ends and their heads almost meeting in the middle. Eventually they have to go in their own cots. At some point they may start to wake each other too but this is more likely to be when they are about 3 months old. Babies are all different – you have to find what works for you and your babies.

Pushchairs and other equipment

There are many double or triple pushchairs on the market, side by side or one in front of the other. I have found that it is useful to find one that folds easily, but if you have space and don't need to be putting them up and down, then go for a sturdier one. It also depends if you are in the town or the country, or have steps, so have someone help you at the shop when you are buying your twin pram or buggy. I think it is as important as buying a car so try before you buy!

You will need at least double of everything on my list on pages 10-11 so take any offers of equipment and help whenever it is offered. A spare pair of hands will help as you learn.

You will find you will have a lot of attention when you have twins; everyone is amazed by them. You can't go for a walk without someone speaking to you. Enjoy it! It's double the fun.

Pets

Dogs and cats are like older children. They have had you to themselves until now and you probably have treated them like your babies, but now the new baby is here.

Try not to push them out as they can react like a jealous child. A dog or cat will initially be inquisitive when you bring your baby home. Your baby will smell of you so your pet will know it is family. If your pet wants to sniff your baby, let them, under your supervision, keeping your baby safe.

Cats

Cats like to curl up and sleep in nice warm places and a baby's crib or pram is perfect for this, so make your crib safe with protective netting or shut the cat out of the room where your baby is sleeping, if you can't be watching them. Cats will naturally begin to stay out of the way if they do not like the presence of the baby, so allow them their space. Keep good hygiene; keep litter trays out of the way, wash hands after cleaning them out and disinfect surfaces.

Dogs

A dog will quickly learn not to jump up or lick your baby, but however much you trust your dog, whatever breed, never leave them alone with your baby. Your dog may not be bothered by a baby crying, or they might be scared by it, or feel protective of it, so your baby could come to harm even if the dog intends no malice.

There have been many stories in the media over the years where dogs have attacked a child or savaged a baby, so NEVER leave a dog unsupervised with your child or baby. Baby gates are a good idea to install before you bring your baby home to give dogs a chance to get used to being separated.

Other pets

Follow common sense rules with any other pets: do not leave them alone with your baby; keep good hygiene and wash your hands after handling pets or cleaning poo or cages. Ultimately, make sure your baby is safe. Never leave your baby unattended with any animal that might harm them.

Remember:

Teach older siblings
to be gentle.

Twins and multiples
are at least double
the fun.

Keep things normal
and be positive.
Don't worry!

Never leave your
baby unattended
with pets.

"Fiona's extensive experience with babies and her confidence make her a very knowledgeable and experienced nurse. For all every day questions, big or small, she has solutions or ways to improve."

Helen, mother of Edgar-Loup, Fiona and Jean-Georges

Problem Solving

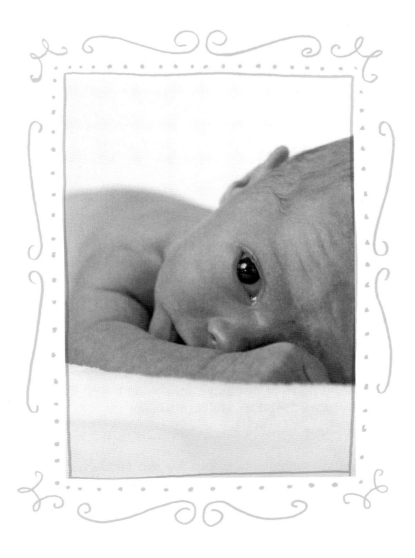

An A-Z of common issues and illnesses.
Planning for a happy holiday.

Common Illnesses and Issues

Babies and children have undeveloped immune systems, which is why we are so careful to observe good hygiene. Common colds and the like cannot be avoided, and in most cases are not serious, so it is good to try not to worry too much.

However, as with any health issue, sometimes secondary infection or complications can arise, so if you are in any doubt as to whether your baby is really unwell, seek assistance from your GP. Trust your instinct. You know your child better than anyone. Babies and young children cannot tell us their symptoms themselves, so it is never bad to be cautious and seek another opinion. Here are some of the most common illnesses and issues your baby might experience.

Baby acne

Baby acne is caused by hormones passed from the mother to the baby. Your baby's face may be very spotty and these spots could be anywhere on baby's face – from the jawline up to the cheeks or on the forehead. This will settle down and disappear after several weeks and is nothing to worry about.

Colic

This can cover a range of meanings, from wind to just an excessively fussy baby. See page 81–82 for a full explanation.

Common cold

Common cold symptoms with babies are the same symptoms as for an adult: a headache, sore throat, runny nose and raised temperature. Unfortunately your baby cannot tell you this! Your baby may not be their normal happy and settled self, they may be crying a lot and seem quite irritable along with a raised temperature and a runny nose. You can give the recommended dose of paracetamol suspension medicine for babies to ease the symptoms, and if your baby seems to have a blocked nose full of mucus, you can use saline drops and vapour rub for the chest and feet to help clear their nose.

Check the age recommendations and always follow the instructions on any medications.

Constipation

Constipation is when your baby is finding it difficult to open their bowels, and when they do the poo is dry and hard, like pellets. This can cause tummy ache and is also very uncomfortable for your baby when passing poo.

It is very unusual for a breastfed baby to be constipated. If your baby does not have a bowel movement for several days whilst breastfeeding, as long as when they do it is soft and normal, it is OK. Sometimes, when a baby has a growth spurt, all of the food is utilised and stored as fat, so there is no waste. Once the growth spurt settles and food increases, bowel movements will be regular again, soft and normal.

Formula-fed babies can sometimes get constipated, especially if changing from breast milk to formula or when the weather is hot and your baby may be thirsty. Formula milk is much more slowly digested than breast milk, so when changing to this, your baby may be a little uncomfortable. It soon passes as your baby gets used to this. If the weather is really hot, your baby may need to drink water in between feeds, as they may be thirsty, not hungry. If your baby is constipated, you can give cool boiled water which should help to keep the motion soft. In extreme cases, please see your GP.

Cradle cap

This is very common and is the build-up of dead skin cells and oils from the skin around a baby's eyebrows, forehead and scalp. If it goes unnoticed, then it can become quite thick and crusty. It can continue into the early years and some toddlers will continue to have cradle cap. To prevent it, you can put baby oil, sunflower oil or olive oil on your baby's head and forehead, leave it to soak for several hours then rub the skin with a muslin cloth gently but firmly. You will notice the dead skin coming off. It is like exfoliation. Then wash your baby's hair. This will keep it at bay if you do it often. If the cradle cap has become thick and crusty, do not pick at it, as this can cause infection. You can also buy shampoo to remove cradle cap and then continue to use it for prevention.

Diarrhoea

Diarrhoea in babies is much looser than a normal breast milk poo. It is very watery, may be slightly green and smell stronger and more offensive than a normal poo. It can be caused by a viral infection, possibly a virus contracted from someone else, or a bacterial infection. For example, if the bottles, teats or dummies/soothers have not been cleaned and sterilised correctly, or you have left warmed milk out of the fridge long enough for bacteria to grow i.e. more than 1-2 hours, then given it to your baby. Newborn babies' tummies are very immature and need to build up immunity to bugs that they come into contact with, so for the first 6 to 9 months it is best to keep everything that goes into your baby's mouth clean/sterile. Continue to feed your baby as normal and give extra cooled boiled water, as your baby can become dehydrated, which is dangerous. If you think your baby has diarrhoea then consult your GP.

Heat rash

Heat rash is probably the most common rash in small babies. Little raised spots pop up anywhere but typically around the back of the neck and shoulders. If your baby seems hot, loosen their clothing and take off some layers.

Hiccups

Hiccups are completely normal. As adults we often get hiccups if we have eaten a big meal or drunk something too quickly. A baby often gets them after feeding. If your baby has fed well and is contented but has hiccups, don't worry yourself about them, just settle baby to bed. He may continue to hiccup but they will subside and baby will fall asleep. If they seem to be bothering your baby, then lift baby and sit them upright for a few minutes until they pass, then settle them into bed again to sleep.

Jaundice

Jaundice is quite a common condition in the newborn baby. If your baby has arrived early, or is small, or has had a forceps or suction delivery, it is more likely that they will get jaundice. Your baby's skin will be yellow, similar to a suntan, and the whites of their eyes will be yellow too.

The cause is your baby having more red blood cells than they need. This can be from the surge of blood from the placenta to baby during birth, before the cord is cut and clamped, or from bruising on the head or a hematoma, caused by suction or forceps, which is trauma to blood vessels under the skin. As the body breaks down these extra blood cells it produces bilirubin. This causes the skin and whites of the eyes to turn yellow.

If this happens more than 24 hours after birth, this is called physio-logical jaundice and is most common. If this happens within the first 24 hours after birth, this is a more serious form of jaundice and will need medical attention.

The only way for your baby to get rid of the bilirubin is for the liver to break it down then pass it to the gut, where it is expelled. When your baby opens its bowels, bilirubin comes out in its poo, and is water-soluble so passes out with urine. Jaundice will not cause any discomfort but your baby may be sleepy. So it is very important to wake your baby and feed every 3 hours.

Feeding your baby frequently will allow the bilirubin to pass out of your baby into the nappy. You want your baby to poo and wee often. Sunlight on your baby's skin makes bilirubin water-soluble so it can pass out in the urine. Undress your baby in a warm room and place them in the natural daylight, not directly in the sun or your baby will burn.

If your midwife is concerned, then she will prick your baby's heel to get a small amount of blood to be tested. Most of the time, feeding frequently and daylight is the only treatment needed but if your baby's bilirubin levels are raised beyond a normal level, then your baby may need to be admitted to hospital where they will be given ultraviolet light therapy. This involves your baby lying under lights in just a nappy, with eyes covered to protect them. This speeds up the process of bilirubin becoming water-soluble so your baby can excrete it. Once bilirubin levels are falling your baby will be discharged and can go home.

If your baby is yellow and sleepy, has dark yellow urine and/or pale stools, tell your midwife or GP.

Millia

These are tiny white or yellowish spots, also called milk spots, on the face, typically around and on the nose. Like baby acne, these spots are caused from hormones passed from the mother to the baby.

Nail infection (paronychia)

A paronychia is an infection that develops next to the fingernail and is quite common on babies' tiny fingernails. Sometimes it just appears for no real reason. The skin peels down the side of the nail and it looks a little red and sore. It may appear as if you have torn your baby's nail off and down the side of the finger, so do be careful when cutting nails. There is no need to do anything at this stage if they are just noticeable. Keep an eye on it and it should heal by itself. Continue with normal cleanliness, washing your hands regularly and cleaning baby's hands when in the bath. If the finger becomes very swollen and/or oozes pus, then it has become infected and you will need to see your midwife or GP.

Sticky eyes

This is very common as babies' tear ducts are so small the tears cannot drain away easily down the duct. It normally corrects itself as baby grows. As long as the white of the eye is not red, this is nothing to worry about. You can wash your baby's eyes by squirting breast milk into the eye or you can put some breast milk onto cotton wool and wipe your baby's eye from nose to ear. Breast milk is good as it is sterile, warm and has antibodies in it, which help healing. If you are not breastfeeding you can use cooled boiled water. Use a separate piece of cotton wool for each eye to avoid passing bacteria from eye to eye.

If the eye is excessively sticky or oozing a yellow substance or is constantly wet and making the surrounding part of the eye sore, or the conjunctiva (the white part of the eye) is red then see your midwife or GP.

Temperature

If your baby is sleepy or irritable, seems unwell and feels a little hot, you need to take their temperature. If it is more than 38°C, you can give children's paracetamol suspension. Give for the correct age. You can buy for 2 months plus and 6 months plus. If the temperature does not come down after 40 minutes to an hour, but has not risen, you can keep an eye on your baby and give a second dose 4 hours later. Encourage your baby to drink to prevent dehydration.

Trust your instinct. If you are worried about your baby then contact your GP.

If your baby or child has a very high temperature of 40°C, and also has cold hands and feet, this can be a sign of serious infection. Seek medical help straight away. Your baby will probably be very lethargic or very agitated.

To take your baby's temperature you can use a digital thermometer, which you put in the ear. It is very quick and easy and beeps when the results are ready in seconds. You can also use a digital thermometer that you place under the arm, right into the armpit, then hold baby's arm down by their side. Wait for the beep and read results. There are also infrared thermometers, where you don't even need to touch your baby's skin. You pass them in front of your baby's skin approximately 2-3 cm away and it beeps with a very quick and accurate reading.

DO NOT use a rectal thermometer. This can cause serious damage to your baby i.e. perforation of the rectum. Use one of the thermometers suggested above instead.

Thrush

Thrush is when an imbalance of the body's natural flora occurs. It is caused by Candida albicans, which lives naturally in our body. Sometimes an imbalance occurs and the Candida albicans takes over.

If your baby has this infection, they will have white spots on the inside of the mouth, inside the cheeks or gums or tongue – not to be mistaken for milk stain. If your baby has just fed and the tongue is white this is normal, but if it is on the insides of the mouth, the tip of the tongue and gums and cannot be wiped away, then this is thrush. Thrush will make your baby's mouth sore and your baby may find it difficult or uncomfortable to feed. They may pull off the breast or teat whilst feeding. It is common in babies and occurs because the baby has low immunity when first born; it is just one of those things which happen. If you are breastfeeding and you or your baby have been prescribed antibiotics for any reason, then this can kill some of the bacteria that we need to keep our flora in balance and this can also cause thrush.

Thrush can reinfect easily from dummies or soothers not being sterilised, so make sure you keep them clean and sterilise them daily.

If your baby has thrush and you are breastfeeding then check your breasts too as you can get thrush in your breast. Your nipples will be very pink and tender, and you may have shooting pains in your breast when feeding. If you suspect that you or your baby has thrush then see your GP as you may need medication.

First Aid Kit

It's useful to set yourself up with a basic First Aid kit that you can grab and go if you need it.

- Thermometer
- Infant paracetamol (only for infants over 2 months)
- Insect repellant
- Insect bite cream or calamine lotion
- Rehydration sachets for babies in case of vomiting and diarrhoea
- Plasters
- Antiseptic wipes

Travelling with Your Baby

Small babies are portable, love being close to their parents and sleep a lot. So take advantage of your baby now – they will never be easier to travel with! However you choose to travel – by car, plane or train, on a long trip or a short one, abroad or in your own country – remember to enjoy it.

What to pack

Try not to over-pack, although you will need clothing for every day of the week. If there are laundry facilities where you are going, then you can plan to wash after a week if you are staying longer. You can pack enough nappies and wipes for the time you are away, or plan to buy when you get to your destination. It's a good idea to take your baby's own bedding and favourite toys, and an insect or mosquito net is essential in some countries so do check advice for your destination.

- Travel bag or hand luggage for your baby
- Changing mat (fold-up or disposable)
- Baby wipes
- Nappies (6, or more depending on length of journey)
- Change of clothes: vests (2), sleep suits (2)
- Soothers/dummies, if you use them (2)
- Bottles with water (2)
- Empty sterilised bottles (2)
- Measured amounts of powdered formula in a dispenser (enough feeds for 24 hours, just in case of delays)
- Muslin cloths (2)
- Rattle or favourite toys, depending on age
- Blanket (it can be cold when travelling with air conditioning)
- Sunglasses and hat
- Pushchair or pram (easy-fold and lightweight)

Extra equipment

If you are travelling by car, you will be less restricted by what equipment you can take, and you can please yourself what time you leave, what time you stop and when to take breaks. The great thing about travelling with a baby is that they tend to sleep a lot as they love the feeling of motion.

If you are taking the train or a plane, and using a moses basket, then you can squeeze in a bouncy chair and activity play gym inside that too. If you are flying, you can book this in as baby equipment or extra luggage. Speak to the airline beforehand, to check what is allowed. Some hotels or villas will supply cots and sterilisers, so check this out too. It will save you having to take too much equipment.

I suggest you take enough powder formula for the time you are away if you are bottle-feeding, in case you cannot buy your usual brand. You'll want at least four bottles, and you can resterilise as you go. A travel steriliser will sterilise one bottle at a time with water and sterlising tablets. It is very small and won't take up much space in your suitcase. You can also use microwave bags, which hold one or two bottles – you put some water in with the bottles, seal the bag and pop it in the microwave for the recommended length of time. Obviously you will need to check if there is a microwave available at your destination if you choose this option.

Nappy changing out and about

When changing your baby's nappy whilst on the plane or train, you can do it either on your knee or across the seat next to you, if it's free, or you can place the changing mat on your partner's knee and change the nappy with your back to the aisle. No one will even know you are doing it.

Of course, there are babychanging facilities in the toilets if you prefer, but quite often there is a queue. Don't worry if people are waiting outside. You need the toilet and your baby needs a clean nappy and needs to be comfortable too.

Remember:

Babies can't say how they feel, so it's OK to get a second opinion.

Try not to worry, but trust your instincts.

Keep a basic first aid kit.

Small babies are great to travel with. Give it a try!

"Fiona's long experience and confidence with babies helps her put each baby in a routine with great ease. I think of her as a 'baby whisperer'; she understands instinctively what a baby needs or wants."

Delphine, mother of William, Alexander and Constance

Daily Routines
Week by Week

Discover your own baby's unique rhythm of feeding, sleeping and awake time.

Week 1

06:30

Feed, halfway through, change nappy. Give the rest of the feed. Burp, then swaddle and place back in basket to sleep. This will probably take up to an hour.

You go back to sleep if you can.

09:30

Feed, halfway through, wash your baby's face to freshen up and change nappy, then give the rest of the feed, burp and swaddle and place back in basket to sleep or just cuddle and enjoy your baby.

12:30

Feed, then change halfway through, then give the rest of the feed. Burp and swaddle to sleep. Continue this sequence all day.

15:30

Feed and change.

18:30

Feed and change.

21:30

Feed, or if your baby is sleeping I would leave them until 22:30 (but no longer than four hours). You want the longest sleep whilst you are sleeping. Swaddle and settle for bed, and fingers crossed that you'll get four hours or more sleep.

If your baby is full-term and healthy, and has no medical issues, let them wake you. They will probably wake at approximately 01:30- 02:00. Then 05:30- 06:00-ish.

Week 2

07:00

Feed, change halfway through, then feed. Burp, swaddle and settle.

You sleep if you can.

10:00

Feed, change, finish feed. Burp, swaddle and settle (or your baby might be awake and want to look around for 10 minutes, then settle to sleep).

13:00

Feed, change, finish feed. Burp, swaddle and settle (or your baby might be awake and want to look around for 10 minutes, then settle to sleep).

16:00

Feed, then halfway through, give a bath, (see pages 48–50).

Then finish feed and swaddle and settle in basket. Your baby will be very tired.

19:00

Leave until 19:30 if sleeping and wake for feed. Change, burp and finish feed, swaddle and settle in basket.

22:30

Feed, change, feed and straight back to sleep.

Now you go to bed too and hope for some sleep. Let your baby wake you.

Hopefully your baby will let you sleep until 02:30 if you're lucky. Feed, change, finish feed and burp. Settle to sleep.

Then 06:00 to 06:30 start your new day.

Week 3

At this age, babies start to show their preferences, so I have suggested three possible options for you – try them to see what your baby likes best.

Option 1

07:30
Feed, change, finish feed and let your baby stay awake, looking around under a mobile or baby gym. Your baby should not be awake longer than an hour and a half from start of feed. They will get very tired.

09:00
Swaddle and settle back to sleep.

10:30
Feed, change, finish feed, burp, and let your baby stay awake for a while.

12.00
Swaddle, burp and settle to sleep.

13:30
Feed, stay awake no longer than an hour and a half.

15:00
Swaddle and settle to sleep

16:30
Feed, stay awake.

18:00
Burp, swaddle and settle to sleep for 45 minutes. This is a power nap just to get them through to bath and bedtime.

18:45
Wake baby, give a bath and massage then feed, at 19:30 if baby can last until then, or feed anytime after 19:00 if baby is shouting for food. Burp, finish feed and settle straight to sleep.

22:30

Feed, change, finish feed, burp, swaddle, and straight back to sleep. All to bed and fingers crossed for some sleep.

Hopefully, wake at approximately 02:30 to 03:00, feed and settle straight back to sleep. Then get through to 07:30 – fingers crossed.

Option 2

07:00

Feed, change, finish feed and let your baby stay awake, looking around under a mobile or baby gym. Your baby should not be awake longer than an hour and a half from start of feed or they will get over-tired.

08:30

Swaddle and settle back to sleep.

10:00

Feed, change, finish feed, burp, and let your baby stay awake for a while.

11:30

Swaddle, burp and settle to sleep.

13:00

Feed, stay awake no longer than an hour and a half.

14:30

Swaddle, settle and sleep.

16:00

Feed, stay awake.

17:30

Burp, swaddle and settle to sleep for 45 minutes. This is a power nap just to get them through to bath and bedtime.

18:45

Wake baby, give a bath and massage then feed, burp, finish feed and settle straight to sleep.

22:30

Feed, change, finish feed, burp, swaddle, and straight back to sleep. All to bed and fingers crossed for some sleep.

Hopefully, wake at approximately 02:30 to 03:00, feed and settle straight back to sleep. Then get through to 07:00 – fingers crossed.

Option 3

If your baby is showing signs of tiredness e.g. yawning or crying, put them to sleep before the times mentioned.

07:00

Feed, change, finish feed then let your baby stay awake looking around under a mobile or baby gym. Your baby should be awake no longer than an hour and a half from start of feed. They will get very tired.

08:30

Swaddle and settle back to sleep. Some babies may take a while to fall asleep but should be asleep by 09:00 at latest or they will get over-tired.

10:30

If you've been waking your baby for this feed at 3 hours (10:00), you could try 3.5 hours from last feed (10:30). Feed, change, finish feed, burp and let your baby stay awake for a while.

12:00

Swaddle, burp and settle to sleep.

14:30 (so 4 hours from last feed)

Feed, stay awake no longer than an hour and a half.

16:00

Swaddle, settle and sleep.

17:00 (2.5 hours from last feed)

Small feed, stay awake.

17:45
Play, gym or chair.

18:45 (1.5 hours from last feed, to stock up for bedtime)
Bath and massage, then feed, burp, finish feed and settle straight to sleep.

i.e. baby will have had more than one full feed but less than two.

22:00
Feed, change, finish feed, burp, swaddle and straight back to sleep. All to bed and fingers crossed for some sleep. Only change nappy if it has poo in it.

Hopefully wake at approximately 02:30 to 03:00, feed and settle straight back to sleep. Then get through to 07:00.

Week 4

At this stage I start to get a little bit strict about waking times. Your baby should be able to be awake for about 1 hour 30 minutes to 1 hour 45 mins at each waking time. However it is trial and error, so if it doesn't work and your baby wakes up in the evening or is awake in the night, then go back to three-hourly and try again in a few more days.

07:00
Feed as usual, burp, nappy change, give rest of feed, then on play gym. Your baby should be ready to sleep after an hour and a half of being awake.

08:30
Settle to sleep. Baby should sleep for an hour and a half.

10:00
Feed as usual, burp, nappy change, give rest of feed then awake/activity.

11:30
Settle to bed in the quiet. If your baby is content and satisfied with food they will lie happily looking around then fall asleep. If baby has been lying happily, then you know they are not hungry. They may start to cry a little when tired but just leave them and they will go to sleep. Hopefully they will sleep for 2 hours. If baby can manage 2 hours then feed at 14:00, but feed anywhere between 13:00 and 14:00.

14:00
Feed as usual, burp, nappy change, give rest of feed, then play gym or bouncy chair, or just a chat with you or friends.

15:30
Settle to sleep. Baby should sleep for an hour and a half.

17:00
Feed on breast or half a bottle and burp – give a small feed.

18:00
Give a nice relaxing bath followed by a massage.

18:30

Give other breast or rest of the bottle then settle to sleep.

19:00

Asleep in bed for the evening.

22:00

Give a very sleepy feed, try not to disturb baby too much. Lift them from the cot, arouse them just enough to get them to feed. Let them feed for as long as possible, burp gently and place them back to sleep. Only change the nappy if it has a poo in it.

Then off to bed and hope baby sleeps past 02:00 to 02:30. Your baby will probably be managing four or five hours from 22:00 by now but don't worry if not, it will come.

Week 5

Your baby should be able to stay awake for 2 hours now; try to get them to do one 3.5–4-hour session between feeds from 10:00 to 14:00, or from 10:30 to 14:30.

07.00
Feed as usual, burp, nappy change, give rest of feed then on play gym or chair. Your baby should be ready to sleep after 2 hours; try to keep them awake. This will make a difference to their night-time sleeping.

09:00 – 10.00
Sleep for up to one hour. Your baby will probably wake after half an hour but if they are sleeping wake up at 10:00. Look out for tired cues after 1.5 hours.

10:30
Feed – this is stretching to three and half hours. Then awake time. Gym chair or under mobile.

12:00 – 14:30
Sleep – baby should sleep well here, up to two and half hours. If they haven't woken, wake at 14:30.

14:30
Feed, burp, change, awake time etc. Try to keep your baby awake until 16:30.

16:30 – 17:30
Sleep.

17:30
Awake. Gym or naked time in bathroom on mat on the floor.

18:00
Bath and massage followed by a feed.

Keep awake whilst feeding, burp well then in to bed for 19:00.

22:00
Lift for sleepy feed. Then fingers crossed for a good night.

Week 6

Your baby should be awake for two hours at a time now. You are now trying to stretch your baby's feeds to 3.5–4 hours. The baby may manage three and a half in the morning then four hours over lunch, then three to three and a half in the afternoon until the early evening feed. Continue this routine for a month or longer, it depends if your baby is ready. By 10 to 12 weeks your baby should manage a four-hour routine, but they must be fed well, be awake and alert at play times and sleep well. But if you have a routine that is working and your baby is sleeping well at night then don't change it unnecessarily.

07:00
Feed as usual, burp, nappy change, give rest of feed then on play gym or chair. Your baby should be ready to sleep after 2 hours. Try to keep them awake; this will make a difference to their night-time sleeping.

09:00 – 10:00
Sleep for one hour; your baby will probably wake after half an hour but if they are sleeping, wake them up at 10:00.

10:30 – 11:00
Feed – this is now stretching to four hours. Only do this if baby is able to. Obviously if they are crying and can't be consoled with playing or distraction then feed at 10.30. Then awake time. (e.g. gym chair under mobile).

12:00 – 14:30
Sleep. Baby should sleep well here, up to two and a half hours. If they have not woken, wake at 14:30.

14:30 – 15:00
Depending if baby fed at 10:30 or 11:00, feed, burp, change, awake time etc. Try to keep them awake until 16:30.

16:30
Sleep for half an hour (longer if needed).

17:00 – 17:30
Awake. Gym or naked time in bathroom on mat on the floor.

18:00
Bath and massage followed by a feed; burp well then into bed for 19:00

22:00
Lift for sleepy feed. Then fingers crossed for a good night.

Weeks 7 to 12

You can follow the routine above for a 6-week old right up until weaning at five to six months. By 10 to 12 weeks your baby should manage a four-hourly routine between feeds, but don't worry if your baby hasn't got to this stage yet and just continue with the three to three and a half hour routine, with a four-hour gap at midday. Again your baby may be starting his/her day at a different time, so adjust this to suit you. For an older baby, you will only need to cut back on nap times to make the routine work. By three months your baby should only need a 15-30min nap in the morning, 2 hours at lunch time and 15 minutes in the late afternoon, but if your baby is grumpy and needs more sleep then let them sleep a bit longer. Just make little adjustments and find what works.

A typical day at 12 weeks

07:00
Feed, awake on gym or chair whilst you snooze in bed or get up and shower; give rest of feed within the hour from when you started.

09:30 – 10:00
Sleep. Half an hour should be long enough; it's just a power nap, so wake them up if necessary.

11:00
Feed, awake playing, then give rest of feed.

12.30 – 14:30
Sleep. Some babies may not need this much sleep, but if baby wakes, try to let them go back to sleep.

15:00
Feed, then play or activity, give rest of feed.

16:30
Sleep fifteen minutes to half an hour maximum.

17:45

Bedtime bath or massage.

Your baby probably won't want to wait until 19:00 for a feed, so feed any time after 18:00 then settle to bed.

22:00

If your baby is still doing the sleepy feed, then give this at 22:00-ish.

Hopefully your baby is sleeping through the night!

Remember:

Make small changes, don't rush.

Every baby is different; use these timings as a guide but listen to your instincts.

For every routine, you can adjust the time you start your day.

If you need to go back a step, don't worry.

You don't have to get up at the first feed time – rest is important for you too!

Keep bedtime feeds sleepy; enjoy activity in the daytime.

A Final Word

I hope you find this book helpful and I'm sure that if you follow some of my tips, you will have a calm and happy baby who plays well, eats well and sleeps well. You and your baby will both know what is happening and what to expect. The first three months, I feel, are crucial. Start as you mean to go on, that way there are no bad habits formed that you will then have to change.

Once you have a routine in place and your baby is eating and sleeping well . . . the rest will follow.

Fiona.

Remember:

Encourage them
to eat well.

Help your baby to go
2.5 to 3 hours between
feeds and then, as they get
older, four hours.

Teach your baby
to self-settle.

Follow your
baby's cues.

Teach them to
play and amuse
themselves.

Give lots
of cuddles
and chat.

Enjoy your baby.

Acknowledgements

A big thank you to everyone I have met on the way to writing this book – without you and the experiences I have had, it could never have happened.

I would particularly like to thank my husband Stephen, and my daughters, Hollie and Charlotte, for being so patient with me whilst I have channeled my energies into my passion for helping new parents with their new babies. I dedicated this book to them because, after all, my passion for babies started with the birth of my own daughters. The trials and joys of parenting made me the person and the maternity nurse that I am today.

My very special thanks go to all of the parents and babies who have allowed me into their lives at that precious time. I cannot name you all here, but you are all very special families, and I feel privileged to have met each and every one of you.

I would like to thank Amy for allowing us to photograph baby Max, who was so happy and content for the photoshoot. And thank you to Simon and Becky at Photopia for being so calm and welcoming and getting the great shots we needed.

And finally thank you to the team at Orphans Publishing for all your amazing help in putting the book together.

Recommended Reading

There's often not much time to do a lot of reading when your baby is small – sleep is always a greater priority. But if you'd like to find out more about any of the subjects I've touched upon, or need more information, then I recommend these books and websites.

Books

Infant Massage: A Handbook for Loving Parents, Vimala McClure, 1982, 2007, Souvenir Press Ltd, London

The Happiest Baby on the Block, Harvey Karpp, MD, 2003, Bantum Dell, New York

The Social Baby: Understanding Babies' Communication from Birth, Lynne Murray & Liz Andrews, 2005, The Children's Project Ltd, London

Your Amazing Newborn, Marshall H Klaus, MD & Phyllis H Klaus, C.S.W.M.F.C.C., 1999, Da Capo Press Books, New York

Websites

I'm available for support and advice via www.fionacooke.co.uk and there's great information on all these websites.

www.iaim.org.uk

www.laleche.org.uk

www.lullabytrust.org.uk

www.nhs.uk

www.thenappylady.co.uk

www.yourbabyspa.com

Index

Your Baby's First Three Months

Use these pages to jot down notes about your unique newborn. Writing things down can help you see patterns you can use to establish a gentle and flexible routine that works for your baby and for you.

A Happy Baby
daily log

time	feeds Breast: L/R | Bottle: ml or oz	sleep Went to Sleep/Woke Up	notes
Morning 6am-12pm			
Afternoon 12pm-6pm			
Evening 6pm-11pm			
Through the Night 12am-6am			